Praise for
Cool, Calm & Connec

"What I find amazing is how simple Martha Straus makes it to become cool, calm, and connected if you fill in the worksheets, do the exercises, and practice the steps that she so clearly outlines in this workbook. Whether your child or teen challenges you with outbursts of anger, intense anxiety, or sullen silences, here is the path to help them regulate those states while maintaining your own calm. Dr. Straus provides easy-to-follow worksheets that help you:

- Analyze your temperament and compare it with your child (you may be different!)
- Identify when (and, even better, how!) to take a break or draw closer
- Find (and use!) good helpers among family and friends.

Even better, she provides several simple-to-apply methods for parents and children together to become cooler and calmer in moments of high temper, such as ways to breathe, get grounded, and verbalize distress. This workbook is chock-full of activities that are calming—and even fun—for parents and children to do together as they find the best steps to calm down when emotions run high.

Dr. Straus writes with a unique voice, filled with such humor, wisdom, and love that readers will find it easy to listen to her suggestions and believe they, too, can accomplish their goal to have a more peaceful household. This is a book I wish I had available as a young therapist and mom!"

— **Dr. Margaret Wehrenberg**, author of *The 10 Best-Ever Anxiety Management Techniques* and *You Can Handle It: 10 Steps to Shift Stress from Problem to Possibility*

"*Cool, Calm & Connected* is an engaging resource that can help parents and caregivers concerned about troubled children, as well as a great tool to supplement trauma-informed, evidence-supported treatment programs. Marti Straus goes beyond most guidebooks by sharing her own feelings and experiences as both a parent and a therapist, making the workbook at once relatable and realistic. Using the activities and thought-provoking exercises in the book helps caring adults become aware of their own reactions and how they can use their feelings to help themselves and their children stay regulated in stressful situations and prevent frustrations, disagreements, and anger from tearing them apart. Straus helps caring adults step back, recognize their own needs and reminders of past traumas, and use their enhanced capacity to help their children. This includes thoughtful and doable guides for what is often so difficult for parents: to choose what to repeat from their own upbringing, determine when and how to apologize for mistakes, learn how to get support and help, and appreciate the value of thankfulness for the joys of parenting, even in stressful times. *Cool, Calm & Connected* is "relational healing for relational traumas" at its best"

— **Richard Kagan, PhD**, author of the *Real Life Heroes: Toolkit for Treating Traumatic Stress in Children and Families* and *The Hero's Mask Guidebook: Helping Children with Traumatic Stress*

"Martha Straus masterfully talks to parents about the importance of modeling emotional connection and regulation, and then shows them how to do it. With empathy, warmth, and a clear understanding of the challenges all parents face, she dives straight into what feels overwhelming and chaotic to families, and then gives the concrete skills and exercises families need to change patterns for the better. We need such a book now more than ever."

— **Lynn Lyons, LICSW**, co-author of
Anxious Kids, Anxious Parents

Cool, Calm & Connected

A Workbook for Parents and Children to Co-regulate, Manage Big Emotions & Build Stronger Bonds

Martha B. Straus, PhD

Copyright © 2021 by Martha B. Straus

Published by
PESI Publishing
3839 White Ave
Eau Claire, WI 54703

Cover: Amy Rubenzer
Editing: Jenessa Jackson, PhD
Layout: Bookmasters & Amy Rubenzer

ISBN: 9781683734079

Printed in the United States of America.

PESI Publishing
pesipublishing.com

Dedication

To my marvelous daughters, Lizzy and Molly, of course

Table of Contents

Acknowledgments

This workbook describes strategies that parents can use to help their distressed kids feel calmer, but it also speaks to the larger need we all have to know there are dependable, caring people out there for us throughout our lives. At age 64, in the midst of a global pandemic, I am newly appreciative of my good fortune to be part of a community, co-regulating at will with members of my family, my partner, friends, colleagues, students, and clients. I am truly grateful for the ways they keep me grounded and connected through their love, trust, and support.

To my family: Most of what I have learned about staying cool, calm, and connected I owe to my daughters, Lizzy and Molly, who gave me ample practice developing the skills in this book. Now, in adulthood, they both take extraordinary emotional care of me too. I am also so thankful for the rest of my family: my utterly reliable and steadfast siblings, Andi and Joe; Joe's brilliant wife, Sally; and my beloved cousins, Billy and Lynne. I remember here, too, my parents, whose dependable love got me started on this journey.

To Mike Fleming: You keep me anchored in safety with your kindness, laughter, and love every single day. If not for you, my Mike.

To my gifted, dependable, and passionate graduate student research assistants: Brooklyn Alvarez, who enthusiastically helped me hatch this book from a couple of lively conversations, suggesting many of the breathing and grounding strategies described herein; and Dana Ludmer, who bravely and intelligently edited later drafts and wrote most of the last chapter. I appreciate all that you have both done to help make this book.

To my Vermont tribe: I love you all to the moon and back. Though we are socially isolating, in my heart I am, right this minute, at a potluck in Sharon's backyard with you.

To my colleagues and students in clinical psychology at Antioch University New England: I thank all of you, especially Barbara Belcher-Timme, PsyD, Vince Pignatiello, PsyD, and Monique Bowen, PhD, for the gift of seeing me as I am.

To Linda Jackson, my publisher at PESI Publishing: I am so appreciative that you sought me out at the Psychotherapy Networker Symposium and believed in this project from the get-go. My gratitude also goes to Jenessa Jackson for her wise and gentle copy editing.

And to the parents and kids who have come to my office yearning for connection: Thank you for not giving up on one another and for sharing your inspirational and transformative love.

Introduction

In my home state of Vermont, where the roads are icy for months on end, we learn how to gently "turn into the skid" when our cars start slipping and sliding. It might be counterintuitive, but that's the way the wheels get in line with the rest of the vehicle so we can stay in control and cruise onward. The first impulse—to freak out, hit the brakes hard, and jam the steering wheel in the opposite direction—practically ensures we'll wind up in a ditch, or worse.

Parenting a challenging kid is a lot like driving on wintry roads. But with some skills and effort, you can learn how to keep steady and remain calm while turning toward, not away from, the struggle ahead.

Using this workbook, you will have the chance to learn about and practice strategies that will help you become more effective at staying cool, calm, and connected with your reactive and distressed child—even when that seems like a mighty challenge. It's part of our job description as parents to try to remain reasonable—to have access to a rational adult brain—when our kids start falling apart. It's a job that appears to take a lifetime of practice to get better at. Over time, though, you'll be able to model how it's done while giving your child the experience of your loving presence that conveys, "I am here. You are not alone. I will help you if I can. *Together* we can become more regulated in mind, body, and relationship." That has to be a relief for a kid who clearly can't pull herself together without your help.

Seeing yourself as a co-regulator is a win-win: You get to be the loving parent you aspire to be, and with your supportive presence, your child learns how to feel better. Indeed, under usual circumstances, your cool adult engagement in itself provides a soothing balm for your child's overwhelming emotionality. Decades of research into attachment and regulation demonstrates that our kids can learn how to calm down *only* after having plenty of experience with the soothing engagement of a caring adult. There is abundant evidence that, from the beginning of life, secure love is the best regulator of all. They can't learn to calm down without us.

Here's how this works: A baby cries and is fortunate enough to get picked up and held. Over and over and over again. The baby is falling apart and the adult's care and safe arms put him back together. Over and over and over again. And only through this ongoing practice of co-regulation can he start to learn what it feels like to be regulated. After a few years of life, the embrace doesn't have to be so physical; when we respond empathically and stay nearby with a struggling older child, she will usually feel "held" by that too.

It feels so good to need someone and to know you can depend on that person when you are struggling. In fact, it's a biological imperative with big lifetime consequences for better or for worse. Babies who miss out on the early opportunities to be held and comforted will spend significant time later wondering who is reliably there for them and whether they are deserving of such care. They can heal and learn this, but they will need even more practice with co-regulation over the years. And they probably won't be able to just go to their room and cool off because they don't really know, in their bodies, what it feels like to be regulated. This need for the comfort of others is, of course, a lifelong desire that doesn't end with infancy. Even when we get pretty good at self-soothing, we still want to know there are people out there who could be there for us and who might help us feel held.

Our White, Western, individualistic culture has gone way overboard in extolling the virtues of self-reliance. Of course, it would be nice if your 5-year-old didn't get overtired and fling himself on the floor at bedtime—but that's an unreasonable expectation for self-control in such a young kid. Similarly, it might be really lovely if your 13-year-old contending with attention-deficit/hyperactivity disorder (ADHD) could just stay off of social media and start her homework without the constant wrangling—but that's actually too much to ask too. Some kids just need more support from caring adults. I recognize, of course, that it's a developmental attainment to be able to take care of ourselves, and most of our children eventually get those skills. But it's no less an accomplishment today to be able to ask for help and to have a reasonable expectation that people who love you will show up and offer it kindly.

There are just two elements you will need to have on board to be an effective co-regulator: (1) the capacity to remain cool, calm, and connected yourself and (2) a variety of skills and strategies that will support co-regulation with your child or teen in the face of escalating fear or frustration. In these pages, you will find dozens of personal and collaborative ideas that can de-escalate different kinds of hot-button situations, whether your child is arguing, raging, despairing, panicking, or shutting down. Help is here for those times when you are at your wit's end, can't deal with the same issue in the same way one more time, and just need something new to try (short of a one-way ticket to a tropical island). *Cool, Calm, & Connected* will guide you through the steps so you can fulfill this essential job as your child's or teen's co-regulator.

One of the many challenges in dealing with dysregulated kids is the unpredictability of what could help them feel and behave better at a given time. Something you do works for a little while and then fizzles or even escalates a situation. A recommendation as obvious and simple as talking calmly might prove to be soothing in one instance and provoke outrage in another. For example, a perceptive child might admonish her oh-so-careful—but furious—mother by saying, "Oh, don't go using your patient mommy voice." Similarly, a teen might react skeptically toward his father's sincere efforts at empathic reflection by complaining, "Don't say that you 'understand' why I'm upset. You *don't* understand. If you understood, you'd let me." That's where this workbook can help: It teaches you how to take a generally more regulated and less reactive approach to these daily struggles, which can make a huge difference in the stress levels for you and your family over time.

If you've been white-knuckling it—gripping the metaphoric steering wheel trying to circumvent the daily icy patches for months or years—your own nervous system will be pretty frazzled even before you start skidding into a struggle and actually need to hold it together. The truth is that it takes an exhausting amount of energy to live on such high alert, whether you are a caregiver or a kid. This is why it is a good idea for you to find a way to become better regulated *before* trying to support your sobbing or raging kid across another icy patch. *Cool, Calm, & Connected* begins with three chapters full of worksheets and reflection activities that can help steady you before you get back on the road.

Luckily, you probably already have some empathic superpowers you can use in a new way to help you handle the next parenting challenge. But first you'll need to become consciously aware of what you may already intuit. Many parents are extraordinarily attuned to their children, perceiving microscopic shifts in mood and emotion. They may even sense and react to changes that denote a shift away from calm and regulation without necessarily registering what's happening. When your baby was small and fussing, you probably transferred him around in your arms trying different positions to settle him down (perhaps while also talking on the phone and making dinner). You weren't thinking, *Now I will dangle him off my hip.* You just did it. When things are going smoothly, it's like that: a parent-child partnership, both making and responding to the adjustments of the other, not even needing to be fully conscious or aware of the interaction. This kind of attunement is a beautiful thing, and it makes a lot of evolutionary sense. We are designed to be empathic, to experience another's feelings as if they were our own, particularly if the feelings belong to vulnerable kids whom we love.

But big feelings in families can be quite contagious. Emotionality can swallow us up before we even realize that our hearts are racing and that we've begun to skid. Honestly, it's hard not to be reactive when it happens so automatically. But when you feel in your body that something bad might be about to happen (even—or especially—if you are 100 percent correct), your own anticipatory anxiety is surely getting stirred into the interaction.

Here's the thing: Your child feels your worry or dread just as much as you are registering her impending unhappiness. This is the challenge of all this gorgeous attunement: Even without conscious awareness, you and your kids are processing one another's emotional states all day long. The solution is to engage less automatically and to be a little more aware of your own activation so you can make choices about how to handle it. *Cool, Calm, & Connected* is a workbook designed to help you become more conscious and intentional—more responsive and less reactive—so you won't heat up the emotionality of an interaction. You'll be able to use your empathic superpowers in the service of turning down the heat instead of adding your own kindling to it.

As you will see in these pages, *Cool, Calm, & Connected* is a workbook for two, designed to help both parents and kids stay on the same team when frustration, disappointment, anger, and disagreement are pulling them apart—again. The worksheets, activities, and explanations that follow aren't complicated, but it will take thoughtful practice for you to master these skills—beginning with a bit of your own work to manage your child's prodigious strategies for getting you to participate in his misery. Through the exercises in this book, you will find out ways to keep your feet planted firmly on the ground, your heart open and full, your eyes on your child, and your rational brain online and ready to think. You'll find that, incredibly, that is sometimes all you need to do to make it quite a bit better.

This book is loosely divided into two sections. The first three chapters are designed to help parents and other caregivers understand the theory of co-regulation and learn to practice the skills necessary to become effective co-regulators for children and teens. For example, you will read about temperamental differences that may contribute to flare-ups with your child and will understand your role in the cycle of escalation. You will learn about how you get hooked by your children and will develop strategies to change direction toward greater calm and connection so you can become your best adult self. Worksheets will teach you how to set intentions for confrontations ahead of time, to use the "react, reflect, respond" approach, to make the most of *adult* time-out, and to figure out what's worth fighting for and about.

The next four chapters are full of worksheets and activities designed for caregivers and kids to work on and practice *together*. Chapter 4 includes activities to help you identify people in your extended family and community who are part of your team, to help your child become more effective at asking for support, and to help you figure out ways to feel less alone in the hard times. Chapters 5 and 6 offer strategies for joint grounding and breathing exercises that can de-escalate and calm an interaction and that keep both of you feeling balanced and centered. Finally, chapter 7 describes arts and crafts projects that support self-awareness and regulation.

Parenting a challenging child can bring you to your knees. The stress of near-constant wrangling is often lonely and exhausting. But there is a steadier, more collaborative path forward. When you learn how to turn into the skid together, you both will gain the traction you need to feel cool, calm, and connected.

1

Co-regulation in Theory and Parenting

Rosa is 11 and in frequent trouble at school. She can't keep her body still or stop talking. She's hot-tempered and jumpy—too often on the verge of sobbing with rage or being buried deep in it. She is so tightly wound up that she misinterprets what's happening around her. She watches others closely and with great intensity but has no dimmer switch. She can't distinguish accidental bumping in the halls from—what feels to her—an attempted assault. She reacts as if she has to defend herself even when she's not being attacked. Rosa also tends to hear simple adult requests as though they are being made through a megaphone. That's because her early life experiences have primed her to expect that people might hurt her. She has become so conditioned to anticipate threats or yelling that she's become ultra-sensitive to perceived criticism. Her sense of impending danger is held strongly in her body, so she's ever on alert. She's safe now, but her body doesn't know that.

When Rosa comes to therapy, she makes herself known partway up the stairs, for example, by loudly admonishing her father for walking too slowly in front of her. She transfers her ire to me before she's all the way in the room, pre-establishing that I have already let her down: I didn't open the door right away even though I must have known she was waiting. The lady I saw before her made the sofa smell like a "gross dead thing." I didn't turn on the overhead light. The game she wanted to play isn't where she last saw it. Or she's so sure I won't let her take home an old magazine from the waiting room (which no one is reading) that she's not even going to ask for it.

My first job is to stay calm and present, offering her compassion and support. I try to show and tell her that her dad and I are here and that she's not alone. I know it's not about me; this level of distress accompanies Rosa throughout the day. I just need to help this anxious child settle down and feel more connected to us. Therefore, my second job is to do something with her in the looming hour that will increase her sense of safety and security. By the end of our session, using a couple of the co-regulation strategies described in this workbook, I can help both Rosa and her father feel a little more attuned to each other. Perhaps unsurprisingly, she glowers at me once again when I say our time is up. She's not a completely different kid, but I can tell that she's feeling more grounded now. Rosa leaves the office easily, even reaching for her dad's hand ahead of a more harmonious walk back down the steep steps.

And then there's Billy, age 14, a small, cautious boy who has experienced more than his share of life stress. But unlike Rosa, he shuts down when he feels overwhelmed, and it's often hard to get him to express himself at all. Billy's parents got divorced when he was very young, but they still struggle over his care. Billy's visitation schedule is complicated and awful—though he'd never say so. He comes to see me because his mother wants him to, while his father has made it clear to us all that he thinks therapy is a bunch of hooey. As with most parts of his life— our sessions included—Billy is caught between his parents, aware that pleasing one means disappointing the other.

In my office, he sits down on his fists and starts bouncing one bony leg while staring flatly into a space above and beyond my head. He's here and not here—the safest option. Sometimes he feels so remote that I am not even sure he has heard me, and I have to repeat my question. If I wait him out, he may—or may not—eventually answer it, dispensing of the inquisition as quickly as he can: "Yes." "No." "Sort of." "I don't know." Billy doesn't actively resist therapy, but he's not taking any chances by getting too close. His first protective strategy is making no waves—hiding in plain sight.

Billy's mom will come with him for part of the hour, and she'll tell us what's been happening that has her worried. He doesn't have friends over. He won't ask for help when he's hurt or in a jam. He spaces out a lot. He plays video games with surprising ferocity, displaying more investment in his virtual quests than he ever shows his teacher or parents. For understandable reasons, Billy's mother is fretful, and she sometimes cries in frustration and despair. When she's emotional this way, he stares at her with wide eyes, his body rigid with anxiety. Her tearful displays frighten him. Most of the time, and by his own acknowledgment, he feels best in my office when he's about halfway present. On a good day, that means I'm not asking anything of him and his mother is not "freaking out."

With Billy, as with Rosa, I begin by making sure I am as available and engaged as I can be. I extend empathy to him about what seems hard at the moment. I watch for changes toward and away from his tendency to shut down under stress. And I try to figure out how to bring him back, getting him connected to his body and to us a little more, a little more of the time.

I also support his mother in her own efforts at learning to calm down. I'm *her* co-regulator too, helping her feel in real time what she might offer in turn to her stressed-out boy. Like most parents, she would be doing a lot better if Billy wasn't such a worry. But her son shouldn't be responsible for her dysregulation. She needs better tools for managing her own overwhelming feelings to become a more reliable ally for him. Throughout our time together, I help Billy and his mom develop and practice the co-regulation skills that will calm them down *together* in the therapy room and then back in their apartment too.

I concede to you immediately that it is a lot easier to stay cool, calm, and connected for an hour a week with someone else's dysregulated child than it is to live with that child. I know that because I'm a parent too, and I remember well what it felt like to be rendered speechless by my energetic and wily 5-year-old who had pilfered scissors to cut up door beads, furniture, stuffed animals, doll clothes, and her own hair…and then denied doing any of it (all probably in the same week that I was blithely handing out many well-measured suggestions to other parents). I know firsthand that it can be absurdly hard to be cool, calm, and connected all the time.

So I hope you will see on the pages that follow that I have significant empathy for you as a parent. The ideas in here have been germinating for a long time. As a clinical psychologist who has worked with kids and families for over 40 years, I have helped many caregivers like Rosa's dad and Billy's mom use their empathic superpowers to become more responsive and less reactive with their kids.

And I have faith that with practice, you too can become an effective co-regulator for your child or teen. In this chapter, you will hear about the basic ideas that underpin this workbook's exercises and activities. Then it will be time for you to roll up your sleeves and learn *how* to become your child's or teen's best co-regulator.

What Is Regulation?

Yesterday, I spent a while in a hammock that was securely fastened between two apple trees. I gazed up at the summer sky, the light dappling the branches and leaves, and filled my lungs deeply with fresh air. I stretched my arms and wiggled my toes. My partner, Mike, was fussing on his computer nearby, and I cheerfully addressed a Zoom question he had asked more than once before. I felt cool, calm, and connected. During that lovely afternoon, I was consciously aware of my thoughts, feelings, perceptions, and behavior, and I could intentionally make the adjustments in my position and attitude necessary to stay that way.

The key thing to know about regulation, whether you are getting back in the zone on your own or with the support of someone who cares—or a little of both—is that your thinking brain has to be online enough for you to be in touch with what's happening inside. That awareness is mighty because it gives you the possibility of modifying your emotions, level of arousal, and body sensations instead of being swallowed up by them all. If you start feeling uncomfortably low or high—in other words, like you might be shutting down or getting too revved up—you still have the time and psychic space to think about what resources you might need to pull yourself back from the brink. This is a skill I will help you practice and learn.

Self-regulation is not the same as self-control, though we sometimes use those terms interchangeably. Self-control is about inhibiting impulses. You want to scream and you don't. By contrast, self-regulation involves identifying the causes of distress in the first place, which reduces the intensity of impulses. You realize that you and your teen are both hungry and irrational, and instead of screaming, you go pile a plate with cheese and crackers. In fact, self-regulation makes self-control possible. By the time you've had a snack, you probably won't feel as much like screaming anymore. And even if you're still annoyed, you'll keep that reactivity in check. Impulses are much easier to resist if we are able to take a moment to reflect on what has us all fired up.

Even if you are feeling pretty wound up these days, it's likely that you are doing your best to feel as regulated as possible. We all have what psychologists call an "optimal arousal zone"— an internal state where we feel connected and present in our life. Do you know when you are in that zone? Some researchers also describe this state as being "anchored in safety." Think a moment about the anchoring people and situations (the who, what, when, and where of it) that help you feel regulated. In my little example, Mike was nearby (who), and I was lying comfortably in a hammock (what) on a summer afternoon (when) in my backyard (where). Ahhhh.

Now you try it:

When I was last in my zone, I _____

_____

_____

(Make sure your answer has *who, what, when,* and *where* in it so you have enough details to remember exactly how that felt!)

Even though those super-calm and relaxed times don't last, we all need to be able to recognize what regulation feels like to be able to get back to that zone again. You will learn more about how to do this in the next chapter, but suffice it to say for now that parenting, and life in general, work a lot better when you can be aware of your inner goings-on instead of reacting emotionally or impulsively saying a lot of hurtful stuff you'll regret later. Regulated people are safe and secure in their bodies and minds, think clearly, feel competent, and are better able to choose a thoughtful way to respond. They have the option of making cheese and crackers instead of escalating a pointless argument.

Self-Regulation Is Hard for Kids…and Adults

I hope you can already see how self-regulation might be a wildly high expectation for younger kids, or for children of any age who are struggling with trauma or high stress; experiencing learning, emotional, or social problems; living in adversity; or contending with any other kinds of developmental challenges. The manner in which we describe dysregulated kids offers a window into how hard it can be for us to live and work with them. For example, these children are seen as angry, explosive, inflexible, hot messes, terrified, disorganized, anxious, defiant, oppositional, noncompliant, distressed, stressed out, tightly wrapped, hypersensitive, fragile, recalcitrant, petulant, obstreperous, insubordinate, manipulative, or just plain bad kids.

Your child is probably on this list sometimes, or perhaps you have some other words you use to tell people about your family's challenges. Whatever words you use, there is plenty of suffering to go around. So if you have a child with problems associated with underlying dysregulation, I want you to know a couple of things: First, I'm sorry this is so hard for both of you, and second, your child doesn't know how to self-regulate and needs your help to learn how. It may seem paradoxical, but our desire and insistence that kids should be able to find that zone of optimal arousal simply because we tell them to actually contributes to child stress and dysregulation. It is basically impossible to *make* someone calm down—no matter their age.

Some parents, at the end of their tether, might even threaten to punish a dysregulated child into giving off the appearance of calm: "Stop crying…or else!" But no one chooses to be dysregulated. And it won't help your child feel more regulated if he is being threatened or banished from sight. Indeed, when you send your overwhelmed child to his room and he screams himself into exhaustion, please know that this bears no resemblance whatsoever to learning how to self-regulate. There may be reasons to separate—for example, the safety of other family members or your own impending loss of self-control—but understand that it is likely that, in this time-out, his body is learning quite the opposite lesson: dangerous disconnection. He may also come to believe that his vulnerability and emotionality are abhorrent to you. That you can only bear being with him in a conditional way, when he's "good."

Other parents may become frantic rescuers when their children get upset. They may rush in to fix what is upsetting them, probably both to alleviate their child's suffering and to do whatever is necessary to stay regulated themselves. Those of us in this situation may reason: It's not worth the fight. It doesn't really matter. Harmony over all. My kid is having a hard time, and I can make it better.

I get it, I truly do. I fully comprehend how it could be that your son is still on a device at 10:00 p.m. even though there's a rule about that or that you ended up doing a whole lot more laundry for a 16-year-old who is perfectly capable of pressing those kinds of buttons too. It may also be that you now have an overflowing basket of unnecessary plastic objects you've purchased while waiting in the check-out line with your child—desperate to forestall a meltdown out in public.

Most of us have been there too, especially when our empathic superpowers tell us that bad things are about to happen: We feel in our own bodies a certain anticipatory dread and move in to do what it takes to keep our kids regulated as quickly and precisely as possible. I'm not universally anti-rescue and actually encourage this strategy over some of the ugly power struggles at the other extreme, especially if those are the only choices available to you at the time.

But I don't see rescue missions as particularly co-regulating. When you take it upon yourself to solve what's frustrating or disappointing for your child instead of supporting and guiding him through life's inevitable hard spots, there is clearly love in your heart. Yet this strategy deprives your child of the opportunity to have his own emotional experience. It conveys to him that you don't believe that he is strong or brave enough to endure or manage those big feelings. He doesn't learn how to rely on you for support as he works through these emotions, nor does he have the opportunity with you to practice the skills necessary to calm himself down. And then you will probably still be walking on eggshells and doing extra laundry next time because this was a short-term fix, not an intervention that will lead to lasting change.

While perfectly understandable, those extreme reactions to challenging behavior almost invariably make it worse in the long run. When a child is behaving childishly or giving signs of an impending meltdown, it may well be frustrating, worrisome, frightening, and distressing—or even enraging—for you. And yet, this is where he is at this moment in his development, even if it's relentlessly stressful and hard for your family. So here's your choice: Keep expecting more of your child than he can deliver, or try something new. No matter how easily dysregulated your child is today, he can learn how to pull it back together with your help. He just can't do it without you.

And let's be honest: Adults have a lot of trouble with self-regulation too, especially once the stress starts pouring on or when a child does any of the hundred things that might push us over the edge. (See exercise 4 in the next chapter for a long list of child behaviors that hook us like that.) There are so many things children know how to do that can trigger us out of the zone into pure emotionality in a flash. Parents often ask, "Why does my child behave this way?" I don't think this is necessarily a bad question, and I certainly sympathize with the fact that their lives would be a lot more enjoyable today if they had a compliant kid. But I have three questions in turn that I think are every bit as important that I want them to consider:

- What is your child trying to communicate to you through this behavior?
- How do your responses affect what happens next?
- What's going on for you that *you* find this behavior so dysregulating?

The point here is not to shame or judge but just to say that we need to look beneath the behavior to understand what it means and to figure out why we get so emotionally hooked by it. In reality, adults don't cope so well with stress either. At some point along the way—considering the incidence of anger, depression, anxiety, terror, tumultuous relationships, addictions, traumas, stress, food issues, depletion, exhaustion, and so on—it becomes incontrovertible that plenty of us are struggling to stay regulated too. The bottom line: It's seldom just about them, and that's why co-regulation is an activity for two.

Co-regulation Is Essential Throughout Our Lives

The ability to self-regulate is entirely dependent upon early and ongoing opportunities to co-regulate with caregivers and people important to us. The best self-regulators out there have social connection and support too. We know now based on decades of research and clinical observation that emotional engagement is fundamental and essential to human survival. We need one another in order to buffer against the effects of stress, from the beginning of life to the very last moments. So even when we grow older and develop many self-soothing strategies, we still have a profound biological need for other people to be there for us through life's more stressful times.

If we try to depend on someone (whether we are 1 or 100 years old), and that person isn't reliable, this can shatter us to our core. For a baby, of course, it can be a matter of life and death. But even later in childhood, and throughout the lifespan, we will continue to feel, in our bodies, that we are in danger when people aren't emotionally available to us. The human brain doesn't make a distinction between emotional and physical isolation. It codes it as danger in the exact same way.

When you come home from work after a tough day, you might want your partner to give you a hug or to ask about what happened. If instead, your partner doesn't even look up from the computer or shrugs indifferently when you start to describe what transpired, it's guaranteed that you will feel hurt. It's not a huge trauma on its own, but these experiences are cumulative. Over time, that lack of emotional presence will take its toll. In your body, it will land as rejection or even abandonment. Indeed, most of us have had the awful experience of having someone physically nearby but emotionally absent—and that's probably even worse than if they weren't there at all.

Now think about your agitated, worried, or fearful child, and consider the kinds of daily disappointments and transitions that might be dysregulating for him and the similarity in how he might be feeling. Of course, your mate probably didn't send you to your room for whining about your day or threaten to confiscate your phone if you didn't hurry up and get a grip. But in pulling away, we create an even greater possibility that we will cause our children to feel emotionally isolated. We *all* need to know our people are dependably there for us when we get stressed out, and we feel a little devastated when they aren't. That's just the way it is.

Self-Regulation Can Only Be Learned Through Co-Regulation

A child's ability to learn to self-regulate is largely dependent upon whether she has been exposed to the gift of co-regulation from infancy. If she was abused or neglected, for example, it is much less likely that she will be able to truly calm down on her own. Only through safe and reliable connection with others can children even begin to recognize what regulation feels like. Babies who don't have attentive and responsive adults will begin their lives contending with toxic levels of chronic stress that can affect them all their days.

These infants spend significantly more time in survival mode. Primed to be ready to fight, flee, or freeze, they have insufficient exposure to feeling safely anchored—they are not in the zone. A baby who exerts all his resources just trying to survive has little left over to attend to or to process what is going on around or within him. Without security and a dependable caregiver, he won't have as much capacity to learn about the world or to find out what it feels like to be regulated. Exposure to early adversity sets children up in distinct ways to have a particularly hard time calming down on their own.

However, even children without traumatic exposure can have trouble self-regulating. I have supported many concerned parents over the years who have done everything in their power to tend to their children lovingly, but the struggle continues unabated. That's because some children have sensitive temperaments or styles that their parents find challenging. They get thrown by life transitions, extreme stress, disruption, dislocation, and loss. Other kids have the dysregulating experience of living without food security, a steady address, or a safe community. Inequitable access to resources and the insidious effects of structural racism contribute to a high level of ambient traumatic stress for many. At the time of this writing, a global pandemic has knocked us all off kilter. And so regardless of the source of the problem—whether it's the individual's biology, their family relationships, the state of their community, or a frightening world—the end result is the same: It is very likely that your child needs you nearby to become a better problem solver and self-soother.

I am reminded of that old saying about the difference between giving someone a fish so he can eat dinner and teaching him to fish so he can feed himself. By way of analogy, like self-regulating, teaching someone to be a competent fisherman has a lot of elements. It doesn't work just by watching someone else do it once or by being handed a fishing rod and being sent on your way. No. Teaching someone to fish involves rowing the boat, demonstrating the best way to put worms on the hook, making sure everyone has life jackets, cheering success (or commiserating when you get skunked), tending to snags and tangles in the line, and helping to land and unhook the catch. But there's more! You still can't eat the fish if you don't know how to clean or cook it. To teach someone to fish—or to self-regulate—well enough to survive, you're going to need to be in the same boat for a long, long while.

Adults Need to Be Regulated to Be Helpful

Anyone who has spent even 15 minutes with a distressed kid knows this all too well: When adults get upset too, it makes things worse. When adults stay calm, the situation is *much* less likely to escalate. So for us to be good co-regulators, we need to have ways to keep our cool, to know what presses our buttons, to have a strategy for staying present and calm, and to have the confidence to try once more after we, even despite our best intentions, have gotten hooked again.

It should go without saying that we ought to be practicing what we preach. Yet there seems to be a disjunction between, on the one hand, our exhortations to anxious and overwhelmed kids, and on the other hand, our own life choices. We know what works: "Meditate!" "Get exercise!" "Spend time outside!" "Get off that device!" "Talk to a friend about things that are upsetting!" "Self-medicate less!" "Stay in the moment!" "Apologize!" "Let it go!" But the sad truth is that most adults are much better at advising their kids about making good choices than they themselves are at following these wonderful and well-researched strategies for living a more balanced life. The data confirming that we should walk the walk is very compelling (not just for our own sake but to better help our children). Indeed, there is even some research out there to suggest that the more we do these things ourselves, the more regulated the kids we live with will become—regardless of what we teach them.

There are lots of ways our children learn to co-regulate from us even beyond the experience of safe anchoring we provide them when they are distressed. In particular, adults model regulation by being in conscious control of their own thoughts, feelings, and behaviors. When we stay cool, calm, and connected with our children, we serve as guides that get them through the rough patch and to the other side. When we stay nearby, we assure safety in our presence and show our children what a calm and safe body looks like. Attendant to this, it is important to underscore again that regardless of what you say or do to help them, your calm presence itself can be regulating.

When we co-regulate, we are also teaching our children that one way to feel less alone and overwhelmed by a big emotion is to identify it. We help them "name it to tame it" when we say, for example, "I can see that you are really frustrated right now." At the same time, we encourage them to ask for help instead of melting down. We might say, "I'm glad you told me you were having a hard time. Let's take a break, and then I will help you finish the worksheet when you feel calmer."

In this way of thinking, children learn the skill of effective dependency. It may be surprising to think of asking for help as a developmental accomplishment, but how many adults do you know who are good at that? Remember, we are wired to need one another. It is a sign of maturity to be capable of recognizing when an obstacle feels too daunting and to then ask for help and feel worthy of receiving it. When we are calm and can stick around to support a distressed child, we provide buoyancy at a time when he feels like he might be drowning.

It can take time and a great deal of patience, but I hope you trust me when I say that functioning as a co-regulator is an excellent investment of your resources: In the future, you will have fewer meltdowns, a happier and better regulated child, and a more loving relationship. It's definitely worth a try to include this identity in your job description.

And remember, we *all* need people on whom we can depend. So make sure you have others in your life who will do this for you too. I will help you expand on this list in chapter 4 when you identify the safe people in your child's and family's life. Who is there for you? Do you have a partner, friend, relative, mentor, therapist, or elder who can provide you with comfort and support when your stress level exceeds your capacity to stay in the zone on your own?

Good Enough for Now

It isn't just our kids for whom we often have lofty and unrealistic expectations; we frequently demand too much of ourselves too. Let's just assume that we are all doing the best we can. What happens for us—and for our most important relationships—when we set the expectations bar at a more realistic level for everyone? Before delving into this workbook or bringing your child into the endeavor, here's a task that will help you start out strong:

Considering the challenges right in front of you and your child, try to think about what's good enough *for now*. As you ponder lowering the expectations bar, please note that in *successful* adult relationships, 70 percent of conflicts never get resolved. Kids outgrow problems more often than adults do, but there is still a real probability you'll be having this struggle again in the not-too-distant future. And rest assured that neuromaturation is on your side. A child's brain eventually grows up and, by about age 28 or so, will likely develop the capacity to problem solve like a fully formed adult brain.

Because you might not get this resolved once and for all, you can feel free to imagine instead what might be good enough *for now*. It is highly likely that, no matter what you figure out today, those dishes will end up in a messy bedroom, electronics will be on when they shouldn't be, and siblings will find a way to drive each other bonkers. Deep breath.

Now finish this sentence:

It would be good enough for now if we could just _____.

Good job. If you need to lower the bar even further, be my guest. Let's start this work with the greatest chance of success we can:

It would still be good enough for now if we could just _____.

You have just set a reasonable goal for yourself and your child. How do you feel about *that*?

In this chapter, you've read about why your job as child co-regulator is so important for both you and your child or teen. As you practice the strategies and skills in the following chapters, I hope you'll begin to have some wonderful experiences of being the cool, calm, and connected parent you've always wanted to be. By helping your child manage overwhelming emotions, you will feel closer and be in the zone together, in real time. Happy fishing!

Taking Charge of Yourself

Sometimes when your child is sobbing or defiant or frightened or nudgy or wheedling, you know just what to do. Maybe you take a deep breath, stop thinking about anything else, and deal. Or maybe you manage to say just the right thing and reason prevails. You can hug and move on. Whichever way the exchange goes, one thing is certain: Even if your child is really distressed, somehow you have stayed in charge of yourself. You're cool, calm, and connected.

Think of a time you felt steady and made it through the morning routine or said no without provoking a meltdown. Write down two or three things you might have done that helped:

When I don't get hooked, I am able to:

1. _____

2. _____

3. _____

Even though there is no magic formula, it helps to think about times you've successfully emerged from the fray without a prolonged or debilitating struggle. Parents who feel embattled often chalk up the easier times to the child's reactions or just random luck—but it's very likely you responded more reasonably too. Consider this little illustration:

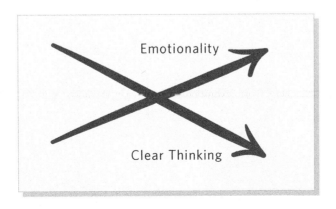

This diagram depicts a direct relationship between how upset you get and how poorly you handle a situation. The more distressed you feel, the less you will be able to think clearly and reasonably. Put a different way: When you can keep yourself from getting activated, you will not be adding your own hot emotionality to the situation. You'll then have a *much* better chance of getting through the struggle. The eight exercises in this chapter are all about you, helping you develop some of the skills, self-awareness, and self-compassion to stay better regulated so you can be cool, calm, and connected even when your child isn't.

Understand the Fit: The Temperament Match Game

Your temperament is made up of characteristics that you were born with. Along the way, you've probably had to make some adjustments so you could manage in the world even if it felt uncomfortable. For example, if you are shy, it's likely that, at times, you've had to make a special effort to speak up or challenge someone. Or if you are very sensitive, you might need a little more time to "just get over" a hurt. Temperament is one way we can think about our tendencies. It describes what typically makes us tick and how we usually handle ourselves in relationships.

Of course, the children or teens in your care have temperaments of their own, meaning that the way they struggle, thrive, and interact with you and the rest of the world is also determined, in some part, by their own temperamental predispositions. The "fit" between a caregiver and a child is made up of many elements, including temperament. When we put two people together, their temperamental styles—whether they are similar or different—help determine how they problem solve, find comfort, and read each other. Understanding and accepting temperament fit is an important first step toward finding relationship strategies that work.

This exercise explores four questions:

1. What is your basic temperament?

2. What is the temperament of the child or teen in your care?

3. How do these match up?

4. What about your temperaments might make it harder or easier for the two of you to communicate?

You can do this activity alone or together with your older child or teen to spur a conversation aimed at better understanding who you each are and what might be more—or less—challenging about your relationship.

By filling in the following 12 temperament scales for yourself and for your child, you can increase your understanding of similarities and differences in your temperaments:

1. **Activity Level:** How active, alert, and energetic are you and your child or teen?

   • How much do you move around when reading, sitting at a table, or attending meetings at work?

   Active ....Settled

   • How much does your child wiggle and move around when being read to, sitting at a table, doing homework, or playing alone?

   Active ....Settled

   • How do similarities or differences in your **activity level** affect your relationship?

   _____

   _____

2. **Biological Regularity**: How easy is it for you and your child or teen to follow simple routines (like keeping consistent sleep and wake times) and to maintain regularity of body functions (like meals and elimination)?

   • How regular are your eating, sleeping, and elimination habits?

   Regular ....Irregular

   • How regular is your child or teen when it comes to mealtimes, a sleep schedule, and bowel movements?

   Regular .... Irregular

   • How do similarities or differences in your **regularity** affect your relationship?

   _____

   _____

3. **Adaptability**: How adaptable and flexible are you and your child or teen when you need to adjust for changes in situations or to make a transition to a different activity?

- How quickly do you adapt to a change in schedule or routine, a new place, or a transition?

  Adapt quickly..Slow to adapt

- How quickly does your child or teen adapt to changes in schedule or routine, a new place, or a transition?

  Adapt quickly..Slow to adapt

- How do similarities or differences in your **adaptability** affect your relationship?

  _____

  _____

4. **Approach/Withdrawal**: How do you and your child or teen initially react to new experiences?

- How do you react the first time to new people, new places, new activities, or an unfamiliar situation?

  Initial approach..Initial withdrawal

- How does your child or teen usually react the first time to new people, new places, new activities, or an unfamiliar situation?

  Initial approach..Initial withdrawal

- How do similarities or differences in your **initial approach** to new experiences affect your relationship?

  _____

  _____

5. **Physical Sensitivity Threshold**: How sensitive are you and your child or teen to each of your sensory channels: touch/pain tolerance, taste, smell, hearing, and sight/light?

- How aware are you of slight differences in noise level, temperature, light, taste, or touch?

  Not sensitive..Very sensitive

- How aware is your child or teen of slight differences in noise level, temperature, light, taste, or touch?

  Not sensitive..Very sensitive

- How do similarities or differences in your **physical sensitivity** affect your relationship?

  _____

  _____

6. **Emotional Sensitivity**: How strongly do you and your child or teen react to the feelings and emotions of others around you?

- How sensitive are you to other people's feeling?

  Not sensitive..Very sensitive

- How sensitive is your child to other people's feeling?

  Not sensitive..Very sensitive

- How do similarities or differences in your **emotional sensitivity** affect your relationship?

  _____

  _____

7. **Intensity of Reaction**: How much energy do you and your child or teen use to express positive and negative emotions? Especially for negative situations that can lead to frustration and anger (perhaps when facing a challenge or not getting your way), how intense is the reaction?

- How strong are your reactions?

  Very intense ....No reaction

- How strong are your child's or teen's reactions?

  Very intense ....No reaction

- How do similarities or differences in your **intensity of reaction** affect your relationship?

  _____

  _____

8. **Distractibility**: How easily do your thinking and attention get interrupted by things going on around you? Do you and your child or teen tend to get easily distracted by interruptions and unexpected activity, or can you ignore them?

- Are you easily distracted?

  Very distractible..Not distractible

- Is your child or teen easily distracted?

  Very distractible..Not distractible

- How do similarities or differences in your **distractibility** affect your relationship?

  _____

  _____

9. **Positive or Negative Mood**: Overall, do you and your child or teen have cheerful dispositions or cranky dispositions? Are you the glass half-full or glass half-empty types?

- Are you mostly in a pleasant and joyful mood or an unpleasant and grouchy mood?

  Positive mood...Negative mood

- Is your child or teen mostly in a pleasant and joyful mood or an unpleasant and grouchy mood?

  Positive mood...Negative mood

- How do similarities or differences in your **overall mood** affect your relationship?

  _____

  _____

10. **Persistence**: How long do you and your child or teen continue to make an effort with a task, especially when the task gets hard?

- How long do you continue with a difficult task or activity?

  Very persistent...Give up easily

- How long does your child or teen continue with a difficult task or activity?

  Very persistent...Give up easily

- How do similarities or differences in your **persistence** affect your relationship?

  _____

  _____

11. **Fearfulness**: How much do you and your child or teen feel fearful, including having a sense of unease, worry, or nervousness related to anticipated pain or distress?

- How fearful or worried are you?

  Very little worry..Constant state of worry

- How fearful or worried is your child or teen?

  Very little worry..Constant state of worry

- How do similarities or differences in your **fearfulness** affect your relationship?

  _____

  _____

12. **Recovery Time:** When you and your child or teen are upset—angry, hurt, disappointed, or sad—how long does it take you to recover to a calm state so you can reengage in the relationship?

- How long does it take you to recover?

  Slow recovery..Fast recovery

- How long does it take your child or teen to recover?

  Slow recovery..Fast recovery

- How do similarities or differences in your **recovery time** affect your relationship?

  _____

  _____

Temperament—and temperamental differences—are such a fundamental part of who we are and how we manage in relationships that these ingredients merit our attention and respect. For example, if you are very persistent and have a child who gives up easily, you will likely have to grapple with that over and over again. Or if you both have very intense ways of reacting, this too will be a big factor in how you trigger each other.

Our temperaments begin to develop even before we are born and stay with us all our days. We need to learn to live with our own—and our kids'—temperaments because this is one part of who we are that isn't likely to change. Here's what you now know is true:

- Temperamentally speaking, I am very similar to my child or teen in these ways:

  _____

  _____

  _____

- I am very different from my child or teen in these ways:

  _____

  _____

  _____

Consider How Old You Feel When You Get Hooked

When our own parents were mean or unfair to us, we may have thought, *When I'm in charge, I will never treat my own kids like this.* Who knew being an adult was going to be such hard work? One mother I know used to tell her defiant daughter, "I can't wait for you to have difficult kids of your own," as though only that kind of payback would level the playing field. When did being a parent become so complicated?

For many of us, part of the complication comes from our conscious choice to react differently to our kids than our parents reacted to us. With noble ambition, we made the decision to offer our kids a relationship that was more validating and connected than the one we had with our own parents. For example, you may have gotten sent to your room or spanked (or worse) for arguing, and now as a parent, you try your best to avoid these punishments, instead using strategies that are gentler or more reasonable. If you are aware that you are trying to make better choices than your parents did with you, describe a couple of examples here:

When I _____, my parent(s) would react by _____.

When I _____, my parent(s) would react by _____.

How are you trying to respond more intentionally to your child as a result of this awareness? For example, when your child argues, do you attempt to understand her perspective or give in to avoid the conflict? What are some things you do differently than your parents did?

When my child _____, I try to _____ instead.

When my child _____, I try to _____ instead.

At the very least, wanting to parent differently than how we were raised gives us a kind of roadmap for what *not* to do. That can help. A lot. Most of the time, though, it's still challenging to handle a distressed or reactive child; you're not alone if you second-guess yourself a ton.

Sometimes it can feel like we are making our toughest parenting decisions via a confused internal committee, made up of an array of enthusiastic advisors we have accumulated over the course of our lives. Here they come: "Set a consequence!" "Ignore it!" "You have a right to ask for help." "Oh, don't get into a struggle on this." "This kid is suffering." "He has it a whole lot easier than I did." "Kids these days need to take on more responsibility." "Kids these days have too much expected of them." "She thinks she's mad; I'm even madder." "I just want to curl in a little ball under the covers." "I have a right to be respected and listened to." "Don't I?"

Where did all these voices come from? What do we do when they are all sounding at once?

You are, of course, an adult reading these pages, but it's useful to see that, right at this moment, you are both your chronological age *and* every age you have ever been. This self-awareness will help you through the noise. The first thing to do is to have some compassion for your own less-mature parts. Sometimes you too may feel the need to stomp your feet, to complain loudly, or to hide under the covers. And, while we are at it, don't most of us have adolescent parts that at least dream of making a few lousy choices or otherwise plan a speedy getaway from the relentless responsibility of being grown up—even if our more responsible adult selves might regret it later?

Of course, it might be easier if we could shush or even banish a few of those highly conflicted voices that live in our heads so we could spend less time flailing, steaming, editing, and criticizing ourselves. But it might be even better to get the inside team together to feel a little more coherent and functional. And that's actually possible to do.

To get the team together, you'll need to do three things: (1) Figure out how old each voice is, (2) find out what each is concerned about, and (3) identify strong qualities you can see in yourself today, perhaps emerging from all this accumulated life experience. These parts are all you (albeit at different ages with various responsibilities), but they are not always as helpful as they might intend and are seemingly at cross-purposes too often. Bringing them on board into conscious awareness can only help.

In this exercise, you will see four human outlines growing in size. Each represents you at a different age or developmental self. You can decide on the specific age of each, but it's good to have, for example, a school-aged you, a teen you, a young adult you, and the present you. Try to respond to the questions under each silhouette according to how you'd think about answering them over the years.

And the next time you get into a struggle with your child, see if you can recognize, without judgment, how far back in age you have gotten pulled. (Some kids are particularly gifted in getting us to regress waaayyy back.)

Pick a common interaction with your child or teen that is challenging for you too (e.g., the morning routine, bedtime, homework, electronics, or a transition). Then write it here:

The struggle that really bothers or upsets me is _____.

Now choose three important earlier ages in your development. Maybe you have very strong memories from your elementary years, or perhaps you went through a significant life event when you were an adolescent. Fill in those ages here:

My age _____   My age _____   My age _____   My age now _____

My response at each age to this struggle would be:

I'd think:

_____   _____   _____   _____

I'd feel:

_____   _____   _____   _____

I'd act by:

_____   _____   _____   _____

What do you notice about how your reactions have and haven't changed? For example, do you still put your hand on your hips and feel like sticking out your tongue? Or do you have thoughts of revenge as you might have had at age 15? Or do you want to throw up your hands and hide in the bathroom? Do you feel like crying the way you did when you were 9 and had a fight? Do you sound like someone you don't even recognize now?

No judgment: This exercise should just get you wondering about how the young *you* thinks, feels, and acts when you get upset with your kiddo. If you can be compassionate with yourself, you might even feel a little better about what happens—*of course* your exhausted 5-year-old self is no match for your energetic 5-year-old child! No wonder it's so hard.

Know and Be Your Best Adult Self

But wait: There's more! Inside your complicated and well-populated adult identity is actually a part of you who is *absolutely* up to the job of dealing with your challenging kid. Let's get you more acquainted with your best adult self.

In this exercise, you will be thinking about yourself at your finest. Reflect on your actual lived experiences—the times you felt all aligned in terms of what you believe and how you acted. Your best self today might also just be a small ember of how you would prefer to live on this earth—a work in progress. Indeed, most of us probably wish our best selves showed up more often.

Consider some of the words and phrases that people use to describe themselves at their best. You might come up with a few other favorite qualities of your own. Feel free to add them to the list too. As you read these descriptive words, think particularly about the kind of adult you would like to be for this child or teen—and even just for yourself! Some questions you might keep in mind include:

- How do I want to see myself through my child's or teen's eyes?

- What do I imagine she'll tell others about me later today or even years from now?

- When *I* look back later today or years from now, what are the qualities I'd like to think I maintained during this interaction?

- More generally: *Which personal characteristics describe me at my best?*

Circle *all* the qualities that might describe you when you are at your best:

Funny	Thoughtful	Attuned	Kind to self
Kind to others	Generous	Forgiving	Understanding
Humble	Reliable	Contented	Loyal
Gritty	Honest	Courageous	Tenacious
Patient	Active	Consistent	Empowering
Dependable	Flexible	Self-disciplined	Curious
Hopeful	Optimistic	Grateful	Respectful
Loving	Altruistic	Balanced	Creative
Silly	Affectionate	Good role model	Good in a crisis
Spiritual	Serene	Apologetic	Sensible
Empathetic	Strong	Proactive	Supportive
Playful	Joyful	Protective	Encouraging
Self-aware	Present	Involved	Adaptable
Good multi-tasker			

Now circle *all* the behaviors you exhibit when you are at your best:

Acknowledge mistakes	Manage stress well
Listen well	Communicate clearly
Promote healthy habits	Have a sense of humor
Demonstrate leadership skills	See child as own person
Take an interest in child's interests	Teach skills and values
Set clear expectations	Set clear boundaries
Work to connect every day	Help with academics
Follow through on promises	Talk about caring
Let kids be kids	Foster interdependence
Foster dependence	Foster independence

Now pick five words or phrases you have circled and write them here. Give an example of a time you showed this quality or behavior. For example, if your best self is "patient," you might write, "When my child couldn't sleep, I rubbed her back and sang to her even though I was exhausted."

Important Quality or Behavior   **Example in Action**

1. _____   _____

2. _____   _____

3. _____   _____

4. _____   _____

5. _____   _____

Great job!!! Take a moment to look over this exercise. Even if it seems silly at first, try to offer that *best self* some encouragement and faith. Our best selves need support too! If this is too hard, you might tell yourself what you would say to someone else who was working hard to be *her* best self—or consider those things you'd like a caring friend to recognize about you.

For many reasons, it is easier for most of us to acknowledge what others do well rather than to pat ourselves on the back. Research supports the common realization that we pay a whole lot more attention to what we don't like about ourselves than to what we do like about ourselves (five times the attention, in fact). It takes effort to change those odds, and here's a start for you. If you still aren't sure how to give your best self some deserved notice, you might find it helpful to complete these sentences:

When I think about my best self, I see that I _____.

If I were recognizing these exact same qualities in someone else, I'd tell

them that they _____.

My best self needs to hear from me that I _____.

I know that, as an adult, I can only be in charge of myself. I have a choice

about how I want to live in the world, and it is important to me to choose to

_____.

Bonus Exercise: Focus on a Small Success

Think about a time that an expected struggle didn't escalate and you stayed relatively cool, calm, and connected. Your best self was rocking and rolling. For example, was there a transition that went smoothly, a simple request that somehow didn't result in a meltdown, something you did that was a little helpful, an intervention you attempted that worked, a family dinner where no one left the table in tears, or a reasonable limit you set that was somehow honored?

Now consider what small valued quality *you* might have embodied that time. If you don't have a clue about what you might have done well in that instance, just try to make something up. It can be hard to see what small things make a difference when we are focusing so much on the big things we expect to go wrong.

The challenge that went well: _____

Maybe this time I was: _____

Own Your Hooks and How They Affect You

We may worry a lot about our *kids'* triggers—often strategizing so they don't get too upset or helping them manage their stress more adeptly. We support them through transitions and disappointments and tune into what overwhelms, distresses, and frustrates them to minimize the meltdowns and misery.

But let's face it: They can hook us in before we know it. If you want to support them effectively, you'll need to pay more attention to *your own* physical warning signs (like tightness in the chest, a welling sense of anger or fear, or changes in breathing) that tell you you're getting too frustrated or upset to engage productively now. Do you know what your triggers are?

There are *so* many things kids do that get adults riled up; the list is impressively long. Here are more than 50 possible hooks. Circle the behaviors that are most likely to distress you right now:

I get hooked when my child...

Throws tantrums belongings	Doesn't respect their
Is rude room	Takes poor care of their
Exhibits entitlement	Interrupts
Swears	Threatens
Yells	Makes false accusations
Embarrasses me or others	Corrects others
Ignores me or others	Acts like an ex-partner
Acts helpless	Has inconvenient needs
Engages in control/power struggles	Is apathetic/uncaring
Gives up	Is resentful
Acts jealous	Acts reckless

Insults others	Acts immature
Lies	Is silly
Dawdles	Is wasteful
Criticizes	Sulks
Acts ungrateful	Has problems with sharing
Is argumentative	Shows bad manners
Acts lazy	Acts bossy
Makes excuses	Cries dramatically
Shows lack of consideration	Is overly secretive
Is prejudice	Whines
Is cruel	Willfully disobeys
Wastes time	Is emotionally manipulative
Is messy	Exhibits passive resistance
Doesn't respect others' personal sleeping space	Exhibits poor eating and habits

Have you thought of some additional hooks that didn't make it to this list? Add them here:

I also get hooked by _____ _____ _____

Try to suspend judgment as you write down more specific answers to these questions:

What are (up to) five things my child or teen does from this list that most often hook me?

1. _____

2. _____

3. _____

4. _____

5. _____

How Do You Know You've Been Hooked?

When you are hooked you will have:

- **Negative thoughts about yourself and your child** (e.g., *He's just trying to manipulate me. She's impossible. I've had it with this kid. I am a terrible person.*)

   I think: _____

- **Difficult feelings** (e.g., frustration, anger, shame, helplessness, guilt, sadness, despair, terror, impatience, hurt all at once: a stress flood)

   I feel: _____

- **Body signs** (e.g., tight muscles, clenched jaw, numbness, disconnection, upset stomach, fast pulse, flushed face, shortness of breath)

   My body signs: _____

- **Distressed behaviors** (e.g., yelling, threatening, swearing, stomping away, becoming aggressive, freezing up, giving the silent treatment)

   I do these things in reaction: _____

- **Other warning signs** (e.g., get upset with other people and pets, use food and substances for comfort, reject help, function less well, take a long while to return to feeling okay, have sleep problems)

   My distress spills over in these other ways too: _____

Isn't it astonishing how those kids of ours have so many ways to get us all bent out of shape? If you know what your triggers are, you may not be able to stay in the zone all the time, but you'll have a much better chance of calming yourself down.

Understand Your Role in the Cycle of Escalation

When your child gets super distressed, what is *your* emotional reaction? Match your *feeling* response to your child's strongly expressed emotion by drawing a line connecting the two:

When my child seems:	I am most likely to feel:
Furious	Furious
Angry	Angry
Explosive	Explosive
Ashamed	Ashamed
Judgmental	Judgmental
Agitated	Agitated
Irritable	Irritable
Hopeless	Hopeless
Fearful	Fearful
Terrified	Terrified
Nervous	Nervous
Annoyed	Annoyed
Sad	Sad
Discouraged	Discouraged
Other: _____	Other: _____

Is there any pattern or connection? Is there any way your reaction amplifies or complements theirs? Write what you notice on the lines provided here.

What I notice is _____

_____

Now imagine this call-and-response as part of an escalating cycle that leads to *both* of you feeling dysregulated. Adding in feelings and behaviors, fill in the cycle below based on what you have noticed.

When my child feels _____,

my child shows me by _____.

Then I feel _____

and react by _____,

which leads to my child feeling _____.

And the whole triggering cycle repeats over and over again.

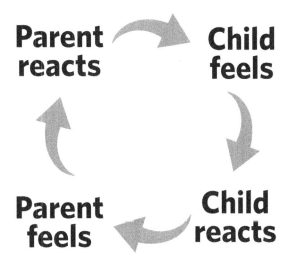

The Extra Baggage We Carry

When you are trying to take care of tough kids, it is easy to imagine that life would be better if they would just shape up. Still, it is worth it to think about you and your child as a part of a larger system too—including the one that began long before she was born.

Do you notice that your emotional reactivity is also part of a pattern in your own life, maybe from your childhood when your own caregivers felt strongly and dealt with you in ways you found upsetting? Apart from your child's provocative behavior, what else do you suppose is coming up for *you* when you respond to your child so intensely?

No judgments: We all carry baggage along from generation to generation, that's just how it is. But what's yours? Take a few minutes to reflect on where your distress might have begun—before your child ever hooked you this way. Try to complete this reflection:

> This is an old hot-button way of reacting for me that began long before my child came into my life. Once I am upset, I get hijacked into old ways of reacting that probably go back to the days when I was a child myself. When I take a step back and think, as an adult, about how upset I get with my child, I can connect it to events from long ago. Looking now at my own feelings, thoughts, and body experience, this is what comes up for me:

_____

_____

_____

_____

Our kids don't intend to claim this baggage, but it is inevitable that they will tap into the well of our lifetime parent-child relationships. Some of the issues you are having with your children belong to them—but not all. For better or worse, living with traumatized, inflexible, or stressed-out kids can be a real eye-opener about our own room for self-discovery too.

---

* Based on an exercise from *One Small Step: Moving Beyond Trauma and Therapy to a Life of Joy* (Dolan, 1998).

Hang Out with Your Wise Old Self*

For this exercise, try to imagine that you have lived a long and healthy life and that you are well into your 80s or even 90s, with all the wisdom that comes with these many more years of life. You have made it through this hard time with your child or teen and are on the other side of the struggle, looking back on those many decades of the past.

Seek the advice and counsel of your older, wiser self, and write down the answer to some questions that you imagine this older, wiser self would tell you:

1. This is the situation that has me very stressed, worried, angry, or upset:

_____

_____

_____

_____

2. What do I need to know about myself to get through it well?

_____

_____

_____

_____

3. What did I do that enabled me to grow old and wise?

_____

_____

_____

_____

_____

4. What advice do you have for me?

_____

_____

_____

_____

5. Is there anything else you know now that you wish I knew already?

_____

_____

_____

_____

_____

* Based on an exercise from *One Small Step: Moving Beyond Trauma and Therapy to a Life of Joy* (Dolan, 1998).

Speak with Your Younger Self*

Now that you have time-traveled into the future, this exercise will help you journey the other way: back in time. The goal is to help you get in touch with what it was like for you to be the age of your child or teen. You will be writing down the answers to some questions that your adult self might find it helpful to remember.

To complete this activity, you will need two writing implements: a pen and a crayon or marker. Put the pen in your dominant hand and the crayon in your non-dominant hand. The dominant hand will reflect your adult self, while your non-dominant hand will reflect your child self. Using the chart at the end of this exercise, use your dominant hand to ask questions and your non-dominant hand to answer them.

Feel free to ask your younger self *anything* you would like to know. If this feels too hard or uncomfortable, you can just ask, "What's up?" or "How are you doing?" to break the ice. Give your younger self a little time to come up with a response. Don't force it; just be curious about what happens next, even if it's really hard or you can't come up with much of a response at all. Don't give up if you find yourself sitting there with a crayon in your hand, maybe even feeling a little foolish.

Sometimes the answers flow freely, and sometimes they don't. But if you come up empty, consider this: The fact that your younger self isn't having an easy time responding might also be worth considering. Being a stressed-out kid is hard work. And if your younger self has a lot to tell you, keep an open mind about how this might help you now. You can also always try another question or revisit this exercise another time to get in touch with your younger self.

Once you have the gist of it, you may even want to seek the advice of your younger self too, perhaps asking, "What would have helped you in this situation?" "What do I need to remember about being (that age) that I seem to be forgetting?" "Is there anything else I need to know?"

Dominant Hand/Adult Questions	Non-Dominant Hand/Child Answers

---

* Based on an exercise from *101 Trauma-Informed Interventions* (Curran, 2013).

Think Backward: Set Your Intention about the Outcome First

Setting an intention is a lot like getting ready to hit the road. Before you go on a trip, it's likely you will plan a bit about what you'll need to pack. You might be sure to have a map or the address entered into your GPS. You'll probably make sure you have enough gas and money on hand, and you'll take stock of whatever else you need to bring. If you are meeting someone at the other end, you might tell them when to expect you. You'll make a note of road and weather conditions so you arrive safely. Even though you might get a flat tire, encounter unexpected traffic, or have to take a different route than anticipated, it will probably still be worthwhile to give the whole journey some thought ahead of time.

Knowing where you are going and how to get there is even more important when you start navigating the hard stuff with your child or teen. Although you can't prepare for every possibility, it still helps to have a good road map for planning tough conversations.

Before heading into a probable conflict with your child or teen, set your intention for the conversation. First, set the intention privately—with yourself—so *you* are clear on what you would like to accomplish. Then, before doing anything else, share it with your child or teen by framing the intention as a hope or a wish. If she reacts adversely, so be it. Remember that keeping cool, calm, and connected is part of your intention too. And if it's still too much for her to handle, offer to revisit the discussion another time. It might go better in an hour, now that your child has a clearer idea of your mission.

In this exercise, you will learn how to create a road map for the destination before embarking on a difficult conversation:

Think of a conflict you recently had that didn't go as well as you'd hoped. Use this opportunity for a virtual do-over by setting your intention *first* this time.

or

Think of a hard conversation you might be likely to have in the not-to-distant future.

The topic of the difficult conversation is _____

When this conversation goes well, I imagine that at the end:

We will have accomplished _____

I will be thinking _____

I will be feeling _____

My child or teen could be thinking _____

My child or teen could be feeling _____

The destination I'm hoping we'll get to is _____

When you set your intention ahead of time, the conversation gets framed by the clear goal you have in mind. You still might not get there, but you are much less likely to wind up in a ditch. Begin with a soft and kind start-up when you state your intention so your child doesn't immediately feel defensive (e.g., "I love you," "I care about you," "I want the best for you," "I am proud of you," "I know this is hard for you"). Then describe the goal simply and clearly. Keep your goal in mind so you don't get distracted and derailed by all the other issues and struggles that arise. You might say, for example, something along these lines:

- "I want to have a hard conversation with you. I promise to listen to your concerns, even if I can't agree with everything. My goal here is that, at the end,… [e.g., we will have a better system for checking in after school; you will know that I love you, and I can't let you do that; you and I will both agree to stay off of the phone during dinner]."

- "I'm worried that what I have to say will be upsetting to you, but if we can both hang in, I have some ideas about how we can fix this."

- "I am not mad. I love you and am frightened. I want to understand how I can support you so you can make better choices next time. This is a hard conversation for us because I have gotten upset about… [e.g., fighting, sexting, school issues] in the past. I'm working hard to see things through your eyes, and my intent is to be helpful."

- "I am on your side. I know that it can be hard for you to settle down at bedtime. I am willing to try to let you stay up later if we can figure out how much sleep you really do need. My hope for this conversation is that we come up with a new bedtime plan that also includes a morning routine plan. My goal is to be sure you aren't exhausted and can get up for school."

- "You know, phones are very tempting for me too, and of course I love it when you text me. But I want to talk about phone use at the dinner table. I wish we could find a way to be at the table with each other without being interrupted by it. Can we come up with a plan?"

- "Wow, it is so hard to have this much to do after a long day at school! Let's think together about all this stress around homework. I hope we can find a way to have fewer struggles and that I can be more helpful to you."

- "I know it can be annoying to have to write thank-you notes, and it feels a little naggy for me to keep reminding you. I want to make it as painless as possible. Can we talk about emailing Grandma? I'd love to have a commitment from you about when you'll make the time, and I'll even do it with you if that would help."

Now you try it:

Soft start-up: _____

_____

We need to talk about _____

_____

At the end of the conversation, I hope that _____

_____

It might be helpful to have your intention in writing in front of you on a table so you stay the course even in the face of your child's clever efforts at derailment. People who are good at difficult conversations keep their loving hopes for a gentle resolution in the foreground. They remember what the point of it all is. They stay calm and focused.

3

Filling the Caregiver Toolbox

Trying to keep cool, calm, and connected when having a conversation with a distressed child or teen can be hard, and sometimes even impossible. The clouds can come on fast. There you are, going about your day. Things seem okay. Your beloved kid comes into the room, and maybe you look up and smile, oh so calmly. Then *kerplooey!* Everyone is shouting at once. You got emotionally hooked during a nanosecond somewhere in there and probably didn't even see it coming. What was it all about? No one can remember exactly.

Of course, you didn't want that to happen. You know it would have gone better if you'd been able to hang onto your best mindful, compassionate, and engaged adult self, as hard as that would have been to do. In this chapter, you'll learn that with practice and some handy tools, you can be that kind of parent more of the time and can have fewer of those upsetting interactions.

Did you know that there's a solid body of research concluding that the ability to feel and stay calm during conflict is a major predictor of happiness in relationships? It's a great skill to learn, and there's no downside to trying. There is, however, a big cost to more of the same. When we get really upset with our children, we become highly reactive, spewing words we don't even mean and will later regret. Or—perhaps worse—we take it to the other extreme, shutting down and going cold.

Though "the silent treatment" means there will be no blowup to get over, that strategy can be even more toxic for your relationship with your child. Here's why: Our kids need to know we love them even—or especially—when they feel miserable and are falling apart. You might not mean to reject or abandon them, but that's likely how they'll feel if you withdraw that way. The bottom line: Your capacity to be both calm and emotionally available under duress lets your child feel the secure love that comes only from regulated adult presence and support. And it is precisely secure love that helps children make better decisions, act more thoughtfully, develop compassion toward themselves and others, contribute more consistently, and be available for stable relationships.

The problem this chapter is highlighting isn't the fact that your child presses your buttons in the first place. We *all* get hooked by our children in unexpected ways; you are not alone when that happens to you. Who among us hasn't felt overmatched by a 3-year-old who won't go to sleep or outsmarted by a teen with a secret social media account?

But parents and caregivers who stay calm more of the time usually have a few strategies they can rely on to keep them from feeling emotionally overwhelmed. These strategies will help them get back on track when too much negative emotion starts to take over. The seven exercises in this chapter should start to fill your co-regulation toolbox—even when that clever and challenging kid of yours has hooked you once again.

Stay Focused and Intentional

When people in satisfying relationships fight, the ratio of positive to negative interactions *in the middle* of a fight is 5:1. (In good times, that ratio is more like 20:1!) This means that for every negative thing you've said or done, you've had five positive exchanges. Think about how hard that sounds! And how cool would it be if you could manage anything like that in the height of a fracas with your child?

Here are 20 positive, counterbalancing strategies used by people who are good at resolving a hot-button conflict. How many do you use? Which could you add on now or with practice?

Place a check mark next to every strategy you use, and then tally up your score:

_____ **Find humor in the situation.** You don't laugh at your child, but you do find some element of the situation that might be amusing to both of you.

_____ **Show respect.** "I can see it matters to you."

_____ **Show interest.** "Tell me all I need to know."

_____ **Demonstrate openness.** "You have ideas I haven't thought of. I want to hear them."

_____ **Provide affection.** "I love how passionate you are about this."

_____ **Are curious.** "I wonder what that's like for you."

_____ **Show a willingness to negotiate (if it's negotiable).** "I think we can come up with a plan that might work for us both."

_____ **Choose words carefully.** "Hang on, I need to think about this a minute."

_____ **Try not to make your child feel cornered or defensive.** "I know you are trying hard too."

_____ **Only focus on one event.** You don't dredge up the past.

_____ **Don't make your child the problem.** It's your problem too and shouldn't be constructed as your kid's character flaw. Think of how you can describe the issue as something that involves both of you: "I can see how my need for a tidy house is sometimes the opposite of your need to have a snack in your room."

_____ **Focus less on your own irritability, frustration, and disappointment in the moment and more on staying present and engaged.** "Let's have a cup of cocoa and talk at the table."

_____ **Don't blame the child for how lousy you feel.** _It isn't your child's responsibility to make you feel better._ "I had a long day, and I need to take the dog out right this minute. I think I'm a little wound up and not at my best right now. Let me have a half hour to regroup."

_____ **Avoid phrases like "you never…" and "you always…"** in favor of simply saying what you need or want to have happen next time.

_____ **Know that you might only have to listen to make it better.** Sometimes simply listening fixes your child's problem of feeling lonely, misunderstood, unheard, or overlooked. Your loving attention is the whole remedy. "This sounds hard. Tell me everything."

_____ **Set expectations for your child's actual developmental skill level.** Thinking about a child's chronological age can get in the way of clarity and empathy. If you view the situation as being caused by your child's lagging skill or immaturity (for example, in reasoning, waiting, perspective taking, or putting feelings into words) and not her willful misbehavior, you will be able to speak with her more gently.

_____ **Take your child's perspective and ask if you have it right.** Keep trying until you really understand. It would be nice if your child could see it your way, _but it is essential you can see things as he does._

_____ **Take a break** if you feel overwhelmed, if the conversation is going in circles, if your child is too triggered to make sense, or if there is no time to get to a resolution. As the old adage goes: When you're in a hole, stop digging.

_____ **Return to the conversation when you are calm to try again.**

_____ **Express your love to your child or teen when it's all over.**

How Did You Score?

0–5: You have some work to do next time, and things will go better if you do. Think about which strategies you could easily adopt.

6–10: Okay, you have the gist of it. Are there some other skills you'd like to try?

11–15: Super! If you want to add to your toolbox, go for it. But you have plenty of know-how to get through a tough patch.

16–20: You truly have mastered attunement and conflict resolution. *You are a pro.*

Bonus suggestion: Try substituting the phrase "for the relationship" for all the dead-end judgmental thoughts you might imagine are true. For example, instead of saying, "He's just doing this… [e.g., for attention, to be manipulative, to gain power, to hurt me, to control me, to get out of taking responsibility]," try this out instead: "He's just doing this *for the relationship*," and see how that changes how you respond.

React, Reflect, and Respond

Once you know you're in a hooked, emotionally charged state, your work involves figuring out how to unhook yourself from it. This requires going through these three steps: react, reflect, and respond.

React: Often, we find ourselves in the middle of a hot conflict or an upsetting interaction before we know it. That makes it hard to prepare and predict. So it's useful to know as soon as possible that you are starting to get overwhelmed, whether or not you saw it coming.

This exercise begins by asking you to take a thorough inventory of what happens to you when you become reactive. In fact, in order to become an expert on your experience, it will help to let your child *really* get to you! You can't get unhooked if you don't know all the details. And reacting is not a bad thing in itself: If you didn't care so much, you probably wouldn't have gotten so upset in the first place.

Feel free to copy your responses from exercise 4 in chapter 2 (Own Your Hooks and How They Affect You), or recall a different time you got hooked, and write down your **reactions**:

What happened that got you hooked? _____

_____

What were some of your negative thoughts about yourself? _____

_____

What were some of your negative thoughts about your child? _____

_____

How did you feel? _____

_____

What were you experiencing in your body? _____

_____

What did you do next that suggests you were hooked? _____

_____

Were there other warning signs you notice now? _____

_____

Reflect: Now let's get you unhooked. To do this, you need to take a deep breath and take a step back. Your reaction was all about you; the **reflection** is all about your child. Your reflective, empathic explanation will help change your ultimate response and will keep you calmer and more connected. When you reengage your loving heart, you can connect more deeply to what's so hard for your child in this world and in this moment.

Here are some reflections you can work toward:

- Believe your child is doing the best he can.

- Open your mind to the idea that *you* might feel and behave the same if you were in your child's shoes. That's empathy in action. Think as a compassionate, objective adult about why and how your child is engaging with you in this unskilled and miserable way.

- Let your own story, expectations, and agenda move to the side for now.

- Feel the love and concern just beneath your reaction.

- Become aware of your body calming down.

- Begin to tell yourself a compassionate story about your child.

Circle some possible *beliefs* your child might have about herself, important relationships, and the world that might explain this behavior:

- I'm not safe.

- People are out to get me.

- People are only nice to get something for themselves.

- The world is a dangerous place.

- No one will help me if I ask.

- No one really cares about me.

- I am not worth caring about.

- I have no control over what happens to me.

- I don't have control over my body.

- Other beliefs: _____

  _____

  _____

Circle some of the *skills* that (despite your hopes and expectations) your child hasn't yet fully developed:

- Identifying, expressing, and managing feelings and body states

- Reacting calmly

- Handling transitions

- Controlling impulses

- Paying attention, especially when worrying

- Thinking logically, problem solving

- Thinking about the future

- Perceiving threat accurately, including reading safety and danger

- Regulating empathic arousal (i.e., cares too much or too little)

- Other lagging skills: _____

  _____

  _____

Now come up with a reflection statement that might lead you out of emotionality and into a cooler, calmer, and more connected zone. Remember, this reflection should result in a kinder, gentler explanation for that challenging and frustrating behavior that was having such a big effect on you!

It is no wonder that my child or teen gets stuck this way in these situations because he believes _____

and _____ and he doesn't yet have the skill to

_____ or _____.

Good job! Now, with this new story in mind, let's get back to *you*: What are some of your more compassionate thoughts about *yourself* that contribute to this situation? For example, perhaps you are exhausted, preoccupied, doing the best you can, feeling unsupported, terrified for your kid, and so on.

Here are two things I know about myself that might also make it hard for *me* in this situation:

1. _____

2. _____

Are you getting unhooked?

- What are you thinking right now? _____

  _____

- How do you feel right now? _____

  _____

- What are you experiencing in your body right now? _____

  _____

Respond: Now that you have **reacted** (gotten hooked) and **reflected** (started getting unhooked), it's time to practice a new way of responding that changes your part in the cycle.

Just as it is important to know when you react by getting hooked and upset, and to reflect on what makes things so hard for the two of you, it is also vital to get ready to try again and **respond** in a cool, calm, and connected way. The next time you start feeling the escalating cycle taking over, remember that you can change it by getting unhooked *before* you respond. Here are some empathic and validating responses you might try saying or thinking instead:

- "I can see this is really hard for you."

- "You seem pretty worried too."

- "This is confusing for both of us."

- "It can be so hard to find the right words to say."

- "I wonder if you think I'm going to be madder than I am."

- "It's really disappointing when you do your best and it still doesn't go the way you wanted."

- "Sometimes we get so upset that the whole day feels like it's ruined."

- "Nothing seems to be going your way this week."

- "It's not fair. I can see how unfair this feels."

- "This is discouraging. I'm so sorry you are feeling hopeless about this."

- "I can see you feel like giving up. But I'm still here, okay?"

- "I'm sorry I wasn't helpful."

- "I'm glad you could be honest with me about how you felt even though it was hard for me to hear it."

- "I see you are overwhelmed."

- "No wonder you are upset. Please tell me everything. What happened next?"

- "I know it can be hard when plans change. Do you want me to tell you as much as I know about the new plan?"

- "This must be so frustrating for you."

Write down and memorize a couple of empathic and validating phrases of your own that would work for your particular child and situation so you can stay unhooked heading back into the conversation. Even if these words sound cheesy and inauthentic at first, they will help to frame your response. People listen better when they feel understood and heard.

- I can see that _____
- I imagine that _____
- It sounds like _____
- I'm sorry that _____
- I wonder if you _____

It is good to remember that you can be empathic and validate your child's experience even if you think his reactions are completely absurd. Seeing the problem from your child's point of view doesn't mean your own adult version is wrong, only that you care about what it's like for him too.

Measure Your Calm

When you are heading into a tough conversation, or an argument has erupted between you and your child, it is important to know whether or not you are capable of meaningfully engaging together. This exercise is important both for you and for your child to gauge whether you both are ready to interact or if you need to take a step back. The more you are self-aware and also attuned to each other's distress levels, the greater the likelihood of a good outcome.

Research findings are clear on this point: If you are in the midst of a heated conversation and your pulse is over about 80 beats per minute:

- You are officially emotionally flooded. Your rational brain has been hijacked and is no longer available to you.

- Only regrettable, emotional, and even crazy things will come out of your mouth until you calm down. Your next words may be forgivable, but you can't take them back.

- The only thing you can do at this point is to stop talking. It should take about 20 minutes, on average, for you to be calm enough to return to the discussion. People vary, so both you and your child will need to figure out the minimum amount of cool-down time you'll need to take before trying again.

In order to reduce your pulse and de-escalate a tough conversation, use this scale:

VERY CALM   1...2...3...4...5...6...**7**...**8**...**9**...**10**   **VERY DISTRESSED**

Know and agree that when either of you are at a 7, you are headed into the emotional flood zone. This means you need to check in with yourself before—and at intervals during—a conflict so you can be sure you are still being reasonable. At least one person in that conversation has to stay cool enough for it to even have a chance of proceeding safely and productively.

Once you have a good idea of how you can use the scale, sit down with your child when things are calm and explain how it works. **Your child or teen needs to learn to use this same scale**. Say that you don't want conversations to feel unsafe or unloving, that you are going to work hard to keep your distress level under a 7, and that you will try to notice if you are getting too upset to be helpful.

Encourage your child to self-monitor and to give you permission to check in with her when things start heating up: "On a scale of 1 to 10, how are you doing right now?" Though this is hard for many kids, it will be useful for them to learn to recognize their own state of distress. Emphasize that feeling overwhelmed and out of control will not be a healthy or helpful zone for either of you to be in when it comes to your relationship or to resolving the problem. Ideally, you will both have the capacity to *self-assess* whether you are calm enough to begin the conversation and to keep at it. But begin by being aware of your own potential for emotional flooding.

Here's a good rule: *Both* of you have the right to take a break when you need it. Your thinking brain needs to be engaged and your heart rate needs to slow down before resuming the conversation. And, not incidentally, that means your child gets to take space too. Anyone can say, "I'm over a 7 and need to take a break" and be granted that space. You can also pause a discussion by saying, "Let's check in. I'm at a 5. How about you?" If you have a child who is so upset he doesn't know it, you can simply claim that *you* need the break. Why not? If you have a challenging child, you probably could use it too.

This cool-down rule can be tough to stick to for a couple reasons. When people are highly activated, it's hard for them to stop engaging. If you or your child are quick accelerators, and go from a 5 to a 10 like a rocket, you might not be able to hit the brake in time. I've witnessed plenty of parents who need to have the last word when going toe-to-toe with their dysregulated kids. If you can learn to just *stop talking* when it's the only sane option, then you will be able to escape the descent into increased emotionality, endless repetition, and general misery.

More commonly, though, a parent wants to call for a break, but the distressed child becomes even more inconsolable. She escalates in rage and terror, continuing to argue, badger, and struggle. Whether or not it is true for you, your child may feel like you are abandoning her in her hour of need—or, at the very least, trying to escape without addressing her concerns.

That's why when you feel emotionally overwhelmed, you should say these three things, in this order:

1. "I love you."

2. "I am feeling overwhelmed and need to take 20 minutes to calm down."

3. "I promise I will come back and try again." (And really do it.)

Measuring your emotionality is a life skill that translates easily to many other kinds of relationships and situations. Indeed, the very act of assessing your level of distress gives you a bit of a chance to step back, take a break, and make an intentional choice about what happens next. And a child who can recognize when she's increasingly anxious, agitated, or heading into meltdown mode will be more likely to get the loving support she needs and deserves.

---

* The is exercise is based on the wonderful work of Ross Greene (2014) in his book, *The Explosive Child*.

Pick Your Battles Wisely: The Three Baskets*

This activity works best if you take some time to figure out your own priorities first and then engage your child or teen in the plan. Imagine there are three baskets of three different sizes where all your possible struggles get stored:

Basket 1: The first basket holds what is essential and non-negotiable. Battles related to health, safety, sexting, and other issues that *have* to be your way all go in this basket. But try to keep it as small as possible. Pick your battles thoughtfully. Once you are clear about what is in this basket, tell everyone in the home. For example, if a basket 1 expectation is that there are no smartphones at the table, you can say, "Remember, it is a basket 1 expectation that no one brings devices to dinner. We aren't having a conversation about this." With basket 1 issues, "no" can be a complete sentence.

Basket 2: The second basket includes any topics that have room for compromise and negotiation. Some typical items in this basket might include rules pertaining to curfew, bedtime, electronics, homework, and clothing choices. Basket 2 should grow fuller as your child matures and demonstrates an ability to handle having more of a say in what he gets to do with his time.

You can say, "This goes in basket 2, so we can talk about how to work it out." The point of having this second basket is to get to a solution without a blowup. It is not designed to cause a power struggle with winners and losers. Optimally, basket 2 discussions can develop the skills of dialogue, negotiation, self-advocacy, and compromise that will be useful now and in the future.

You don't give up the option of moving the item down into basket 1 if your child goes into meltdown mode instead of sticking with a productive discussion. Try to calmly say, "I want to give you a say in these plans, and I am prepared to work with you to come to a solution we can both live with. However, if you yell and swear at me, I will take this to mean you aren't ready to have that conversation right now." If your child pulls herself together, do try again. Basket 2 gives you the chance to co-regulate and problem solve, and it is definitely worth pursuing.

Basket 3: The third basket holds everything else and should be as big as you can safely tolerate. If you can let go of the struggle, do it. The goal is less friction in the home and more opportunity for peaceful engagement. For example, can you give up wrangling about certain chores and expectations, swearing, bedtime, bad music, or unhealthy snacking? Once you get the swing of it, you might be surprised how nice it is to lower the "expectations and conflict bar" for a time in the service of love, sanity, and harmony.

If you can't let go of an issue, that's okay. You certainly don't want to put any issues in basket 3 that will make you bitter and resentful or that you really can't let go of. But when you are able to put things into basket 3, you create greater balance in your family life. You can be firm when you need to be and flexible when it is called for. Just imagine how great it will be once you've figured out and explained your baskets to your child, and you can cheerily say, "Oh, sure! That's a basket 3 issue. Have fun!"

Try to come up with a preliminary set-up for your baskets by figuring out how to sort your struggles into these three baskets:

Basket 1	Basket 2	Basket 3

Don't worry if you change your mind and move items around. That's an important part of the exercise too. Picking battles involves clarifying your own values. What really matters most to you? It can take some time to set it up the way that feels right. In addition, kids grow and change, so baskets can too. And if you have a spouse or partner, it may take time to get to a sufficient level of agreement so everyone in the home is using the same baskets.

---

* Based on the wonderful work of Ross Greene (2014) in his book, *The Explosive Child*.

Make the Most of *Adult* Time-Out

Time-out isn't really all that effective for kids. In fact, for traumatized, anxious, and stressed-out children and teens who struggle with regulation, it's too often experienced as a toxic punishment. Most of us know we are dreaming if we expect that dysregulated kids will somehow use time-out for productive self-calming and restorative reflection on how their behavior affected others. It is much more likely that they are busy screaming themselves into terrified exhaustion, trashing their rooms, or plotting revenge.

Happily, though, there is plenty of convincing evidence that time-out is a very useful tool for adults to use on *themselves*. Sometimes we just find ourselves at the end of our ropes too. *Someone* in this downward spiral really needs to chill out, and instead of sending our kids to the corner or to their rooms, we can consider taking an adult time-out instead.

In this light, time-out is best understood as a kind of pause button for a difficult moment in a relationship. It's an opportunity for a caregiver who is stressing and regressing to get a grip to try again more intentionally. And that's reason enough to learn how to do it—but here's the bonus effect: In taking an adult time-out, we can also model *self-awareness* and *self-control* by acknowledging that we are overwhelmed and need to calm down.

It is good to let kids know ahead of time—when everyone is calm—that you will be trying to time *yourself* out. Explain that, during your time-out, you intend to stay nearby, you will not be abandoning anyone, and you will only reengage in the discussion after you cool off.

You can use the scaling strategy to say, "I am over a 7 and getting too upset to keep talking now. I need to take a break so I can be thoughtful and loving in this conversation." Or once your child understands the circumstances in which you will be self-administering a time-out, you can simply say, "I'm sorry, but I need a time-out right now." Evidence suggests it can take around 20 minutes to calm yourself down, sometimes more or less. You will get better at it with practice and will learn how long you need to feel reasonable again.

Here are some signs that indicate you may need a time-out. Check the ones that apply to you:

_____ You're emotionally a wreck.

_____ Your muscles are tense, your heart is racing, and your head is throbbing.

_____ You feel an urge to run away and maybe not come back.

_____ You can't think straight, thoughts are just flying around in your head.

_____ You want to yell or scream (or you have already started yelling and screaming).

_____ You make threats you don't mean and won't follow through on.

_____ You feel like crying or start to cry and just can't talk.

_____ You want to shake or hit someone or something.

_____ You start slamming objects down or want to break and throw things.

_____ You don't even like your child anymore, not one bit.

_____ You get very short-tempered with *other* people, pets, appliances, etc.

_____ You clam up in a rage, retreating from an increasingly distraught child.

_____ You don't recognize yourself.

_____ You just can't cope one more minute this way.

_____ Other: _____

_____ Other: _____

When you take a time-out, you will use it to regroup and get back into connection with yourself and your child. *Time-out isn't supposed to be punishment for anyone.* It's also not just an opportunity to check your phone or to do a chore. The intent is to focus on feeling and thinking better so you can do better next time with your child.

Make the Most of Your Time-Out

Let's say you get the sense that the situation is devolving and it's time for a time-out. First off: Congratulations on having the self-awareness to know you needed a pause and to ask for it. You stopped a situation from escalating, and now you won't say and do things you might regret later. Now what?

- Focus on breathing and relaxing your body. Figure out what combination of breathing, grounding, and relaxation strategies work for you so you can calm down even a little. You will find many calming suggestions throughout this workbook.

- Try to drop off those negative thoughts about yourself (*I'm the worst parent. I just can't take it anymore*) and your child (*He's trying to destroy me. She's crazy*), or how right you are to be upset and how wrong your child is to be making such irrational demands—because even if it's true, it won't be helpful.

- Try to regain compassion for yourself and for your child. Understand and appreciate how hard it is for both of you.

- Make a plan for how you'll approach the situation when you leave your time-out.

- When you return to the child—and the triggering issue—tell him again that you care about him and are trying your best. Explain why you took a break and how some things you did were helpful in calming you down (so you can model and explain how self-soothing helped you). Apologize with an explanation if you have reason to.

- For example, you can simply acknowledge that you were tired, irritable, preoccupied, or unprepared for what happened and shouldn't have reacted that way. If you take responsibility for your role in the escalation, this isn't making excuses for anyone. You might simply want to apologize for getting more upset than the situation warranted. Tell your child that you are working on becoming less quick to react and, though you might lose your cool some other time, you will continue to practice what you preach.

- If taking an adult time-out doesn't help much, or you seem to need many such breaks across a day or week, you may want to talk to a therapist or a counselor about your stress level. It could be that your ongoing dysregulation means you could use a bit of extra support for what makes these interactions so very challenging for you.

Adult Time-Out Worksheet

The next time you take an adult time-out, use the prompts on this worksheet to help you regroup. By the end, you should be cool, calm, and connected—and ready to try again.

1. **Rate your distress:** On a 1–10 scale, with 1 being very calm and 10 being very distressed, I am at a _____ right this minute.

2. **Describe the triggering event:** What happened that led to my time-out?

   _____

   _____

3. **Take care of yourself:** It is time to focus on getting calm. Decide which brief calming activities are most helpful to you. Try to have a good list of strategies on hand for your time-out. Some people have a little time-out box filled with soothing scents, photos, a poem, or affirmations. Others have a chair or a corner of their room that feels like a safe and cozy nest. What calming activities work best to help you feel better (e.g., breathing, grounding, relaxing, distracting, looking at pictures, stretching, imagining a comforting scene, counting)? Pick a couple from each category here for starters:

   - **Calm your mind**

     o Focus on an image

     o Count backward

     o Think about a place or activity in great detail

     o Notice everything in the room that is a certain shape or color

     o Listen to soothing music

     o Look at photographs of peaceful times or places

     o Other: _____

- **Calm your body**

  o Tense and stretch your muscles

  o Jump up and down

  o Focus on breathing

  o Wash your face

  o Do a yoga pose

  o Stand like superman

  o Dance

  o Other: _____

- **Soothe yourself**

  o Say something kind and reassuring to yourself

  o Think about something you are looking forward to

  o Read a poem

  o Find a meaningful affirmation

  o Remember what you love and that you are doing the best you can

  o Remind yourself that this too shall pass

  o Other:_____

4. **Make sense of your reaction:** Write down your reflections about what happened that led to your self-time-out.

- What bigger meaning did I create about the situation? _____

  _____

- What other opinions and explanations was I adding? _____

  _____

- What did I think my child's or teen's intentions were? Do I still think that? _____

  _____

- What was I feeling in my body? _____

  _____

- What emotions did I have (e.g., anger, sadness, guilt, worry, frustration, rage, terror, misery, numbness)? _____

  _____

- What do I tell myself when I have these feelings? _____

  _____

- What has helped in the past when I felt this way? _____

  _____

- What do I wish I'd remembered about myself that would have been helpful? _____

  _____

- What do I wish I'd remembered about my child that would have been helpful? _____

  _____

5. Be compassionate to yourself and your child: Write down your reflections about what happened from a compassionate perspective.

- I now have these kind and reassuring words for myself that acknowledge how hard this is for me:

  This is my struggle: _____

Can you find the calm inside to also extend this compassion to your child or teen? Write that down too.

- I now have these kind and reassuring words that acknowledge how hard this is for my child:

  This is my child's struggle: _____

6. Take a couple more minutes to settle down: Sit quietly. Breathe out the anger and frustration. Breathe in love and compassion. Check in with yourself:

On a 1–10 scale, I am at a _____ right now.

7. Set the new intention:

- When I try again, what will help us most? I will work to keep the stress level low and be most effective and kind by _____

  _____

8. Return to this worksheet when you can: Finish by writing a couple of sentences about how it all turned out.

- Did the time-out help? What happened when you reengaged with your child? _____

  _____

- What seemed to work? What didn't work? _____

  _____

- Any final thoughts, with 20/20 hindsight, about how you can handle this event better next time? _____

  _____

Learn to Apologize: The Difficult and Necessary Art of Telling Kids You Screwed Up and Are Sorry

Most of us grew up with parents who didn't apologize to us. Indeed, a lot of people—not just politicians—really seem to struggle with how to go about apologizing, as well as asking for and granting forgiveness, even in their adult relationships. It's quite possible that we never learned much about apologizing if we grew up without hearing how it is done. Incredibly, some people find a way to go through their whole lives without acknowledging they have caused harm to someone they love. A rupture without a repair is a loss for everyone concerned.

However, it is a fact that in all intimate relationships, people miss the point, hurt one another, don't show up with their best selves, or otherwise contribute to a break in the connection. Ruptures are as inevitable in our relationships with our kids as much as with any of our other intimate bonds. Of course, with good reason, most parents demand their children apologize to others—so it makes great sense that we endeavor to show them how it's done.

There is *no* downside to learning how to apologize, and there are many, many advantages.

For example:

- Your child learns that we all make mistakes and have a responsibility to fix them.

- When we hurt people, even if it's unintentional, they still feel bad. Acknowledging that hurt and trying to make amends helps people feel better.

- Apologizing is nurturing.

- Apologizing offers the chance to reconnect.

- When we apologize, we are modeling good behavior.

- Apologizing acknowledges our imperfection (very important with anxious kids).

- Apologizing supports real authority.

- Apologizing reestablishes dignity for a child who feels invalidated.

- Apologizing requires full engagement with someone you love.

- Apologizing repairs relationships.

- Apologizing promotes mutual respect: no double standard.

- Reconciliation builds empathy.

Here are 10 situations that probably call for an apology to your child:

1. When you yell at him or punish him harshly

2. When you shame or embarrass her

3. When you blame him for something he didn't do

4. When you lose your temper or behave in an overly emotional manner

5. When she sees you behave in a rude way toward others

6. When you don't keep your word

7. When you hurt his feelings

8. When you forget, break, or damage something important to her

9. When he had reason to expect you'd do something you've done before and is upset you didn't act as you had in the past

10. When an interaction feels bad to *you* even if she hasn't said she is upset

How to Do It: The Basic, Four-Step Unconditional Apology (Not Too Much, Not Too Little):

1. Say the words: "I'm sorry. Please forgive me."

2. Describe what happened: Link the behavior to the apology. Be very specific: "I should not have assumed you forgot to take the dog out."

3. Ask or wonder how it felt for them: "I can see how that would hurt your feelings. Is that why you are mad now?"

4. Offer to repair or say what you'll try to do next time: "Bingo and I are so grateful for your help. Next time I will just ask if the dog has been out."

That's *it*.

Do *not* keep talking, except maybe to say, "I love you." Do not give in to the temptation to explain, to make excuses, or to defend or justify your error. These "apologies" become non-apologies very rapidly. Finally, no "buts…" (As in: "…but you forgot to take Bingo out so many times that I could easily have been right.") It's just a simple apology best done without blaming or shaming anyone. You are human. You made a mistake. You are sorry for that. Done…This gets easier to do with practice.

If you can't apologize right away, no worries. After you have calmed down, do it then. With apologies, it really is better late than never. And if your child can't forgive you right away, that's your child's choice. Give him time if he isn't ready. In the meanwhile, you can forgive yourself.

Now try this exercise: Think of a time when you did something that was upsetting for your child or teen. Write down a simple apology to say what you are sorry about:

I'm sorry I _____

_____. I wonder if you might have felt _____ or _____ because of that. Next time I will _____

_____. I hope you will forgive me

for _____.

Practice the Attitude of Gratitude

It sounds funny to say, but in psychology, gratitude is a hot topic. A big and growing body of research is demonstrating that you can get all kinds of physical, emotional, and spiritual benefits by spending a little time each day finding reasons to be thankful. Gratitude is a growth industry. And it's good for you.

One of the most effective and well-studied gratitude exercises simply requires you to write down *three things* you are grateful for at the end of the day—and to say why they happened and how they happened. The more nights you do this over time, the greater your happiness will be. No kidding—research shows that you could be up to 10 percent happier in just a few months!

A great family dinner-table activity is to go around and ask everyone about the best thing that happened to them that day. It is good for all of you to express gratitude out loud. Or if you'd like a little more structure, make some copies of the exercise here, and fill it in with your morning coffee. Try to get your child in on the practice with you! Your whole family can become more regulated with a daily practice where you recognize your individual and collective good fortune.

I am grateful for my family because _____.

Here is something good that happened today: _____.

I am grateful for my friendship with _____

because _____.

I am grateful for who I am because _____.

It is silly, but I am grateful for _____.

I am grateful for my child (or parent) because _____.

One more thing I am grateful for is _____.

4

Finding More Safe People

We evolved by living in communities where extended networks of adults were nearby to help raise the kids. Parents were not supposed to have to go at it alone in a small apartment or at the end of a dirt road with no help in sight. Beyond a doubt, isolation makes everything worse. *All* of us need reliable, safe people around who are on our *team*—especially kids who have endured early adversity, as well as their invariably overwhelmed caregivers.

Of course, parents are the head of the "team" if they feel up to it, but high-need, high-risk, and high-anxiety children and teens need more adult support, and that's a fact. In rural and underserved areas, finding more caring, safe teammates can take additional effort. Gathering a group of invested adults around your child—whether formally or informally—is often a daunting task. But it's an endeavor that's both necessary and worthwhile.

In this chapter, I'll help you tackle some ways to find and build a community to support your family. Community support might comprise extended family members, school employees, mentors, and friends. The community could develop into a formal support team—like social workers, court representatives, and therapists, as you might have in an official wraparound program—or it can evolve as an informal, but defined, network—like aunts and uncles, grandparents, family friends, neighbors, coaches, and religious leaders. Remember, being able to rely on others is a sign of maturity; there is no downside to *effective* dependence. Every person on earth needs support and love. (Go back to chapter 1 if you forgot why this is so essential.)

This chapter includes five exercises that focus on finding and building a team of adults around dysregulated kids, teens, and their caregivers. These worksheets explore both the quantity and quality of connections, provide strategies for increasing the number and presence of involved adults, and help you identify supports for the life transitions to come.

Find Helping Hands

Can you name five adults who you and your child agree are "there for" them? Perhaps you have your own network of friends, family members, and colleagues who take care of you, but they aren't really a big part of your child's or teen's life. If that's true, wonderful for you! Let's then just focus on whether there's enough back-up for *your child*.

Five supportive people is a fine number to begin with—fitting tidily on the digits of one hand—but in the life of a developing child or adolescent, it's still pretty minimal. If you don't have even that much back-up, it's no wonder you feel overwhelmed! This activity can help the two of you think about and work on this issue.

Try This Activity

Have your child or teen trace the outline of his hand up to the wrist on a piece of paper. This is his helping hand. Talk about the idea of the "helping hand" and how it can reach out for support. It's a nice metaphor for something we all need. Of course, hands also harm and oppress. With older children and teens, you can talk about hurtful hands if it seems important—you might even go on to make another hand of the people who aren't safe or reliable—but the main focus of this activity is to work together to find *good* support for your child and family.

Together, try to come up with five adults in your child's or teen's life who are important allies and have his best interests at heart. If you easily have five adults other than you in mind, feel free to write your own name on the palm of the hand. Discuss each person as you decide whose names you might print on the outlined fingers. If your child comes up with someone who, on deeper consideration, isn't really going to lift them up, or if he wants to include a same-aged peer, remind him that this activity is for finding *helpful adults*. It's also important to have supportive friends, and he is welcome to outline a different hand later, adding five same-aged peers to the team if he so desires.

Have your child write the phone number of each adult by the name (or, if he has a smartphone, he can just enter the numbers into his phone for easy access). Let these team members know they are part of the helping hand. Make sure to put the hand drawing on the wall or the fridge or someplace you can both get to easily. When we feel alone, sometimes we forget that we have people out there, just a call (or text) away. The outstretched hand is also a reminder to stop and reconsider our loneliness. When we feel overwhelmed, this hand tells us there are people in our life who care.

Here are some ideas for your child's helping hand:

- Other parent, step-parent, or foster parent

- Extended family members (e.g., aunts, uncles, grandparents, adult cousins, adult siblings)

- Family friends

- Neighbors

- Therapist(s)

- Teacher(s)

- Other school adults (e.g., counselor, nurse, coach, staff)

- Other professionals in your family's life (e.g., social worker, pediatrician, youth worker, juvenile service officer)

- Community supports (e.g., coaches, music teachers, YMCA workers, after-school staff, Big Brothers/Big Sisters, mentors)

- Religious leaders

Here is an example of a finished helping hand:

When you think about the people to include, here are some qualities you might want to discuss. Not many helpers will have all of these attributes, but the best ones probably have at least 10 of them:

_____ Has a good understanding of the hard times I have had in my life

_____ Doesn't blame me for the hard times I have had—and knows that blame isn't helpful

_____ Can think about the people who have hurt me or have left me and can understand I might still have loving or protective feelings toward those people

_____ Doesn't always have to be right—can compromise and take other people's ideas into consideration

_____ Doesn't always make it about himself, can be a good team player

_____ Doesn't gossip about my life

_____ Communicates clearly (or might be able to learn to be a good communicator)

_____ Can follow through on things she promises to do

_____ Makes time to talk with me, meet with me, and be part of my team

_____ Builds my confidence

_____ Expresses his support and appreciation of me

_____ Builds connections to other helpers

_____ Allows me to express my feelings

_____ Is consistent and reliable

_____ Is (mostly) patient

_____ Gives me more chances to try again when I make a mistake

_____ Is likely to say, "Of course!" when I ask her to be part of my helping hand

After a few months, you might want to revisit the helping hand to be sure it includes the most up-to-date, top five supports. And when you swap in a name, plan to add on a running list of *both* the older and newer helpers. Struggling kids usually feel lonely too much of the time. If your child believes she doesn't have anyone in her corner, these names can be a nice reassurance that she has at least a handful of reliable adults in her life.

Create Support Circles

In this exercise, you will help your child or teen think about who supports him in his life (both adults and peers) and how close he feels to each person. Your child will place himself in the center of the circles and will write the names of other people in the rings that increase in distance from the center. Feel free to suggest people who have cared for your child and to whom he might feel close, including friends and family. If there aren't many people (or many close people), or if you disagree about how close someone seems to be, just observe your child's work and allow him to depict his relationships with the people in his life. No need to persuade him that he has more support or that he is closer to more people than he says he is.

This activity should generate a conversation no matter how many people your child is able to draw into the picture. Here's an example of a child who has a favorite brother, one close friend, a distant friend, a nearby father, and a mother from whom he feels distant.

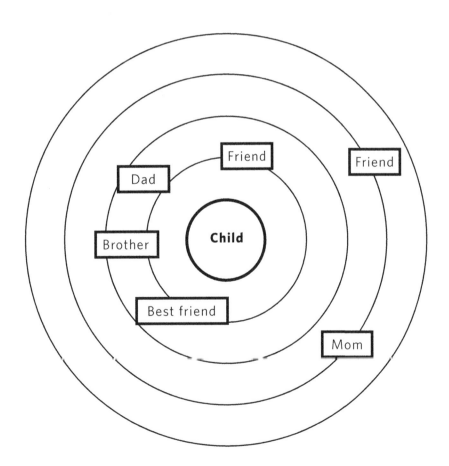

With younger kids under about age 12, it can be plenty to just think about how close they feel to people in their lives. You can keep the activity fairly simple, locating family and friends around the page. For older children and teens, you can get a little more detailed. Have your child use four different colored pencils or markers to distinguish among these different types of trusting relationships:

1. **Intimate connections:** First consider the family members and best friends with whom a child or teen may have the most loving relationships. These are people who feel like anchors, even if there is conflict between them some of the time.

2. **Friends and extended family:** Are there other friends and extended family members who matter but who might not, at least for now, be the closest allies? Perhaps imagine an important life event, like a graduation. Are there people with whom either of you might want to share the news? Are there people with whom your child has fun, with whom he might consult when he feels stuck or confused, whom he considers to be "like family," or who would give him a hug when he needed it?

3. **Community:** If your child or teen engages in activities outside of school, she may have peer and adult acquaintances she would like to include on her circles, even though she might not know them well.

4. **Professionals:** Here you can include other people who might not be as close to your child but who still matter, like teachers, school counselors, therapists, pediatricians, social workers, coaches, or anyone else in a formal role with whom your child may feel a trusting connection.

Now examine the finished product together and explore what you see. What features are particularly noteworthy and stand out for you? For example, are there many or few supports? Just one or two close names? People included or omitted that surprise you? Where are you and others situated in comparison to one another? Here are some ways to reflect back to your child what you notice:

- "I see you have just a couple friends to whom you feel close. Do you sometimes wish for more friends, or is that a good number for you?"

- "Look how close you feel to Grammy. Can you say what makes her so trustworthy to you?"

- "When you look at this picture, what do you notice about the support in your life?"

- "Do you notice anything special about how close or far away most of the people are?"

- "I'm sorry there aren't very many people out there right now to whom you feel close. I think this is something we might try to work on."

- "Wow, you have so many people in your life!"

The last part of this activity involves looking at each person in the circles and deciding if your child or teen wants to be closer or more distant from that person. Ask your child to draw an arrow extending to the point that she would like to be more or less intimate. For example, the child in the previous example might draw arrows indicating that he would like his friend to be a little closer and his mom to be a lot closer to him. A circle template is provided for you on the next page.

How Close Do I Feel To the Important People In My Life?

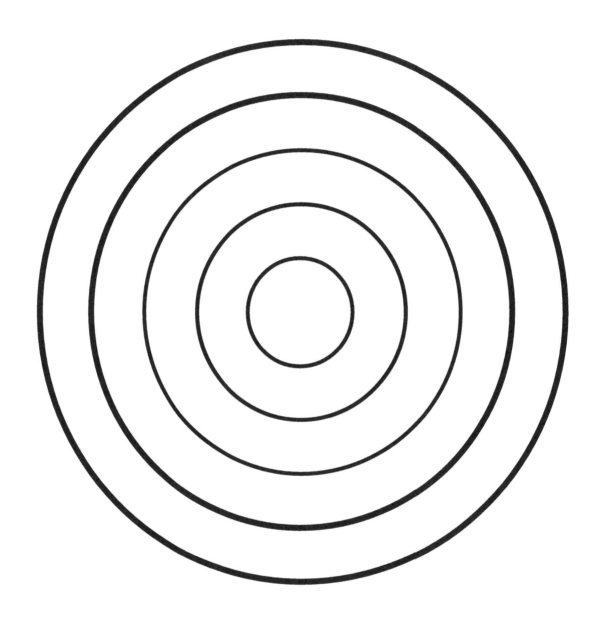

Tell a Life Story of Helpful People

One of the most important elements in becoming more regulated is having a story about your life that makes logical and emotional sense and sharing it with someone who listens and cares. For kids who have endured trauma and loss, this story will inevitably have parts with great disappointment and sadness. Some of it might be disorganized and feel confusing to them. But that's seldom the *whole* story.

In this activity, you and your child will begin to retell your child's life history organized along a timeline. Everyone needs a coherent "story of me," one that has some linearity, to help them understand their lives. The narrative will highlight people who have been helpful, supportive, and kind along the way. Your own understanding or memory of the early years will help fill in parts your child may not know or remember. The goal isn't to sugarcoat or ignore the bad parts but to give attention, year by year, to some of the important people who have been helpful.

Here is a template to help guide your child's narrative. If your child is young and hasn't gone through all these stages mentioned, you might ask her to make predictions into the future. For example, you could ask, "When you turn 9, who do you think will be at your birthday? What kind of cake do you think you'll have?" Or feel free to simply leave those questions blank.

My Full Story

When I was a baby, _____ took care of me and fed me.

When I was 2 years old, _____ helped me feel better if I had a nightmare or couldn't sleep.

When I was 3 years and got sick, _____ took me to the doctor.

When I was 4 years old, _____ knew what my favorite thing to play with was. It was _____.

When I was 5 years old, _____ pushed me on a swing or did something outside with me. We played _____.

When I was 6 years old, _____ helped me learn something I didn't know how to do (like tie my shoes or do homework). This person taught me _____.

When I was 7, _____ taught me something fun to do outside (like riding a bike, catching a ball, fishing, or playing other sports). This person taught me _____. The best thing I remember about this is _____.

When I was 8, _____ took me on a trip somewhere fun (out to eat, to the zoo, to a movie, or someplace else). We went _____.

When I was 9, _____ celebrated my birthday with me. The best part of my birthday was _____.

When I was 10, my favorite movie was _____. I watched it with _____.

When I was 11 and I got hurt or sick (fell down, broke a bone, scraped a knee, bumped into something, had a fever), _____ helped me get better.

When I was 12, the person who I relied on the most was _____. Some of the ways I knew this person was there for me included _____.

When I was 13, the person who knew me best was _____. My favorite memory of being with this person is _____.

When I was 14, I had help getting ready for high school from _____. This person helped by _____.

Other people who have made a positive difference in my life over the years include:

_____. This person helped by _____.

_____. This person helped by _____.

_____. This person helped by _____.

If these memories lead to questions, conversation, and other reminiscences, all the better. The more richly remembered narratives are also likely to be the most meaningful and coherent, so this activity can be a springboard for an important discussion about your child's identity and their caring relationships.

Make a Shield of Belonging

Long ago, knights put images on their shields to give them courage. These images included representations of their families, sources of strength, and symbols of belonging to help them go bravely into battle.

Though we may not be living in medieval times, we still have shields to protect us from life's difficulties and dangers. These shields are made up of connections. It is our community that shields us from harm because with them we are less alone. They help us grow stronger and feel safer. When we are part of something bigger—like our family, a circle of friends, the natural and spiritual worlds, or other groups with whom we share interests and passions—we too can bravely confront our life's challenges.

In this activity, you and your child will develop a shield to depict the connections in your lives that provide protection for your family. On the next page you'll find a shield template divided into four different sections. Discuss what should go in the four different parts. Think about the traditions, activities, interests, and personalities that make you strong together. How you would best like to represent these qualities on the family shield?

Our Family Shield Of Belonging

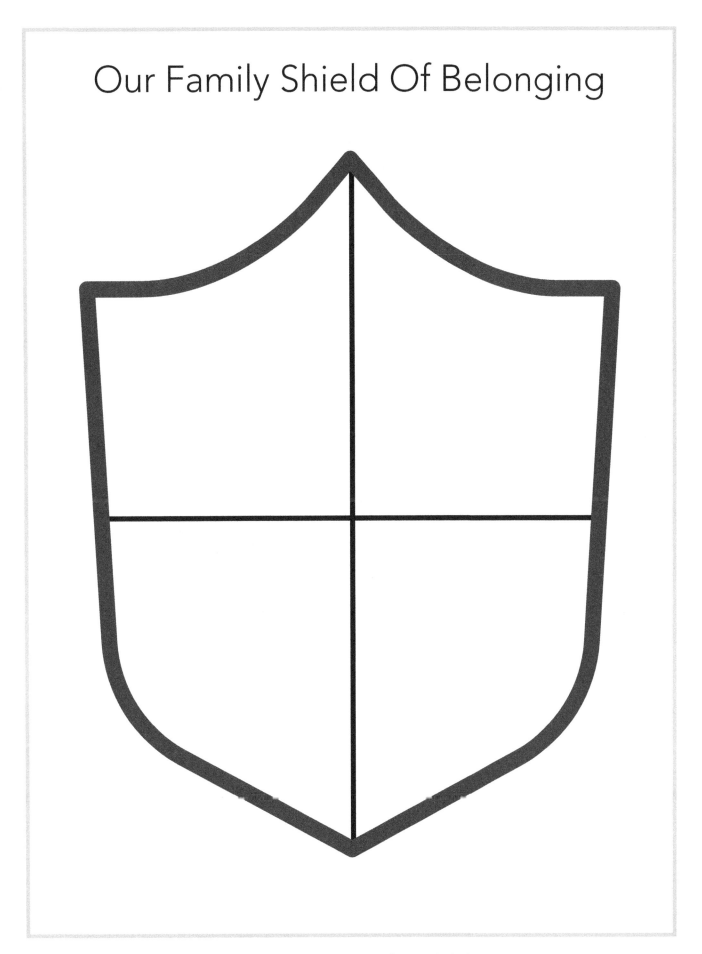

Learn to Ask for Help

Being able to ask for help when you need it is actually really hard for many people—adults and kids alike. There are jokes about people who have gotten lost because they didn't want to ask for directions and plenty of stories about people making all kinds of mistakes they would have avoided if they had just reached out to someone who knew what to do.

This is important: Being able to ask for help—to know when you can't do something on your own, to see that there might be someone else who could support you, and maybe most importantly, to believe that you deserve this care—is a life skill worth learning and developing.

In this activity, you and your child will discuss why it is hard for each of you to ask for help, name some times when you were able to ask for help and get it, and figure out how you can ask for help in the future.

What's good about asking for help? Here are 10 reasons. Do you have a favorite reason? What is it? Can you think of others?

1. You can get things done better and faster.

2. You can be better at separating what you know from what you don't know.

3. People like to help, so it could make your relationships better.

4. It's good to practice gratitude, and we feel grateful when we receive help.

5. You can find out that people really do care about you when they say yes to your request.

6. Knowing what to do—and not feeling alone while you do it—reduces stress and can make you healthier.

7. It's a sign of humility and strength (not weakness) to need other people and to know they need us.

8. At many points in our lives, we *all* need help, so it's good to learn how to ask for help.

9. It's a relief to know that you don't have to be the one who has to do or fix everything.

10. You'll have more time to do other things.

Can you think of a time when you asked for help and it really made a difference?

Parent _____

Child _____

What's hard about asking for help? Here are 10 possibilities. Can you think of more?

1. **Fear.** People don't ask for help because they are afraid:

   - They might be rejected.

   - Someone might think they are weak or dumb.

   - They could be told no and then feel even worse.

   - They are giving away power to someone else.

   Are you or your child afraid of asking for help for any of these reasons?

   Parent _____

   Child _____

2. **Past experiences.** In the past, you tried to ask for help and something bad happened.

   Do you have a story about a time when you asked for help and didn't get it?

   Parent _____

   Child _____

3. **Shyness.** Some people feel shy about asking for help. It's embarrassing or just really hard for them to get up the courage to speak up like that.

Discuss a time when you felt shy for this reason.

Parent _____

Child _____

4. **Not wanting to impose on others.** Some people don't want to seem too demanding or needy.

Discuss a time when you didn't ask for help because you didn't want to impose on someone who could have helped you.

Parent _____

Child _____

5. **Family messages.** Some families give different messages about whether kids are supposed to ask for help. They may have unspoken rules about helping children over a certain age or varying expectations for the independence of boys and girls. Kids usually learn early on which adults will be more generous with time and effort. What do you think your family policy is about whom you can ask for help?

Parent _____

Child _____

6. **Quid pro quo.** Quid pro quo means, literally, *this for that*. Sometimes people don't ask for help because they think they'll be expected to do a lot more in return.

Describe a time when you didn't ask for help because you thought you would owe someone too much for it.

Parent _____

Child _____

7. **Guilt.** Some people feel guilty or ashamed about asking for help.

Discuss a time when you have felt guilty about needing help.

Parent _____

Child _____

8. **Feeling like a burden.** Some people worry that the people around them have lots of problems too. They don't want to ask for help because that might make it harder for others.

Can you think of a time when you didn't ask for help because you didn't want to bother someone who had problems of their own?

Parent _____

Child _____

9. **Feeling hopeless.** Sometimes people don't ask for help because it feels pointless, and they think other people might not be able to help them anyway.

Can you think of a time when you didn't ask for help because you didn't think anyone could help?

Parent _____

Child _____

10. **Rugged independence**. Some people see themselves as the type of person who can figure things out, muscle through hard times, and hang tough no matter what. Asking for help would mean they aren't as self-sufficient as they wish they were.

Can you think of a time when you didn't ask for help because you wanted to feel strong and independent?

Parent _____

Child _____

How do you ask for help? Asking for help is hard to do *and* it's good to do. Here are 10 ways you might try it even if you have worries and reasons for why it might not work out. Can you think of more?

1. **Make a good match**: It's good to know who can help you with particular things. For example, your older sister might be really good at figuring out friend issues at school, and your mom might be very helpful with long division. Your uncle could help you throw a ball farther, and your school counselor could give you strategies for managing your anxiety about next year. Or you might have someone in your life who is ready and willing to help you with lots of things!

I need help with:	Someone who might be able to help me:
Homework	_____
Friend problems	_____
Body worries or confusion	_____
Scared feelings	_____
Overwhelming feelings	_____
_____	_____
_____	_____

2. **Be specific and thankful.** If you know exactly what you need, you will have a much easier time getting people to jump in. For example, if you ask, "Can you help me clean my room?" you might be less successful than if you ask more specifically, "Can you help me fold the clothes that are on my bed?" Or if you say, "Can you help me with the first paragraph of this paper?" you might have a better chance of getting support than if you ask someone to write the whole paper for you. Don't forget to say thanks when you get the help!

What do you think about this suggestion?

Parent _____

Child _____

3. **Imagine you are worth it.** Whatever has happened in the past to make you wonder about or doubt your worth, your life will be better if you come to trust that you deserve to be helped. What does it feel like to say, "I deserve to get some help when I need it and ask for it"? There are lots of things you do every day that you can do on your own, but no one can do *everything* on their own.

    What do you think about this suggestion?

    Parent _____

    Child _____

4. **Believe that other people want to help you.** Right now, have a conversation about whether this is true. Even if you were hurt or rejected when you asked for help in the past, there are still people out there who want to support you now. It can be an act of courage and a great life changer to find this out.

    What do you think about this suggestion?

    Parent _____

    Child _____

5. **Think about the problem you need help with as though it is a *separate* thing that the two of you are going to deal with.** Maybe imagine it sitting there in a chair, not a part of you at all. You could even give it a name. How about "Homework Hornet" or "Nervous Nellie"? You aren't the problem who needs help, *it* is. Have this problem ask for help instead of you, and see if you can be part of the solution! For example, together you might decide how to reassure Nervous Nellie about the upcoming school concert: "Should we try to tell Nellie that all the kids will be singing loudly and that you can sing softly if you want?" or "Would Nervous Nellie feel better if we do that breathing exercise that you like?"

    What would you name the problem you are dealing with?

    Parent _____

    Child _____

6. **Ask at a good time.** When asking other people for help, it's good to have a conversation with them when they are available. Sometimes it might be beneficial to begin your request by acknowledging that the other person is busy: "I can see you're busy making dinner now, but can you help me practice my lines later?" Think about something you might need help with and whom you might ask to do that.

Can you think of a good time and a bad time to ask this person to help you?

Parent _____

Child _____

7. **Think about the possibility that waiting until things get worse will, in fact, be worse for you and the people who care about you.** Ask yourself, *What will happen if I don't get some help with this now?* For example, if you don't practice your lines for the play, you will have a hard time at the rehearsal. Or if you don't get the dirty laundry on your bed sorted out, you might have nothing to wear to school tomorrow.

Can you think of a time when it would have been beneficial to have asked for help but you didn't?

Parent _____

Child _____

Let's apply this to your life right now. What do you need help with right now?

Parent _____

Child _____

What might happen if you don't ask for it?

Parent _____

Child _____

8. **Try the five-minute rule.** If you have been stuck trying to do something for five minutes and aren't making any progress, give yourself permission to ask for help.

   What do you think about this suggestion?

   Parent _____

   Child _____

9. **Think about the ways different people might be helpful.** There are different ways people can be helpful. Here is one way to categorize the helpers in your life:

   • **Talkers**: People who are easy to discuss things with and who can help you talk through something

   • **Feelers**: People who can laugh and cry with you and who can really understand how you feel

   • **Doers**: People who don't necessarily want to talk at length or be emotional but know how to get things done

   Have a conversation together about the different people in your lives, and come up with examples of helpers in these three groups.

   Talkers: _____

   Feelers: _____

   Doers: _____

10. **If you are shy or have trouble directly asking for help, think about texting, drawing a picture, or writing a note**—anything that gets your request to the right person. In person or in writing, here are some different ways to actually explain what you need:

- "I tried _____ and _____, but I'm still stuck. Could you help me, please?"

- "I understand _____, but I'm confused about _____. Could you please explain it to me?"

- "I feel _____ right now trying to do this by myself. It would really help me feel _____ if you would do this with me: _____."

- "When you have time later, can we _____ together? That would be really helpful."

Which of these 10 suggestions could you imagine yourself using?

Parent _____

Child _____

Which of these 10 suggestions would you be willing to try?

Parent _____

Child _____

The next time you waffle about asking for help, consider these three compelling reasons to give it a try: (1) Life is short, and it doesn't have to be this hard and frustrating. (2) Many people like to help. We even have an expression for it in psychology: "the helper's high." (3) Everyone else on the planet needs help sometime. Why not you?

5

Grounding Together

When distressed children and teens become triggered, they lose their sense of calm very, very quickly. It can feel—often to caregivers too—like they are suddenly hanging on through a roller coaster ride of overwhelming thoughts, feelings, sensations, and memories. Without external structure and support, this stomach-churning trip can be quite lengthy, lasting on average over 45 minutes. Strapped in tightly and hijacked from the present moment, some dysregulated kids can even find it difficult to move. Others may flail in a desperate, fearful attempt to fight or escape.

It's typical—and understandable—for caregivers to get caught up in the whirl. They often experience their own powerful emotions and a sense of helplessness that reflects that of the kids in their care. With two on board, the roller coaster picks up speed. Until someone slows it down enough to get back on solid ground, it can become a miserable and frightening experience for everyone involved.

In this chapter, you will find a set of 10 structured and semi-structured grounding exercises designed to help kids *and* caregivers co-regulate when either or both of them are beginning to feel the roller coaster ride commencing. You will be encouraged to use the exercises to calm yourself and to reconnect to the present moment *prior* to engaging your child or teen in grounding with you. Once you are more regulated, you'll have a better chance of offering your child comfort and support for returning to the here and now.

Grounding will help you and your child place your feet—sometimes quite literally— squarely on the floor, redirect your minds to your personal and relational experiences in the present moment, and distinguish between activation (the *feeling* you are unsafe) and a distressing event from the past (in which one or both of you *was* actually unsafe). Grounding gives you both a chance to calm down, to get back into the present moment, and to move forward.

To become more grounded, it helps to know the difference between too much emotionality (hyperactivation) and too little emotionality (hypoactivation) because that will determine whether the energy needs to go down or to come up.

Here are some signs that your child or teen is *hyperactivated*, in which case you need grounding to bring energy *down*:

- Anger and angry outbursts (verbal arguments or physical fights that involve yelling, throwing or hitting things, or pushing or hitting other people)
- Extreme irritability or anxiety

- Panic
- Difficulty calming down on their own
- Reckless or self-destructive behavior
- Fear (of things or people) that results in their constantly scanning the environment for danger
- Exaggerated fear or startle response, jumpiness
- Clumsiness (more than usual)
- Increased distractibility and lack of focus
- Trouble settling down for the night

Here are some signs that your child or teen is *hypoactivated*, in which case you need grounding to bring energy *up*:

- Depression or sadness
- Low-grade irritability or nervousness
- A "numbed" emotional state
- Low energy
- Low enthusiasm
- Low motivation
- Withdrawal from family or social relationships
- Hypersomnia (excessive sleeping)
- Loss of appetite
- Shutting down in the middle of a conversation
- Spacing out
- A sense of being "there and not there"
- The appearance of just going through the motions

Are *Your* Feet on the Ground?

It always helps when the adult is more grounded than the child. Even if you are starting to get dysregulated yourself, it will still be really useful for you to know that you can say yes to these three questions when your child starts to go off on the ride:

_____ Am I currently grounded enough to lead the exercise?

_____ Can I invite my child to participate with a gentle and respectful tone?
_____ Will I be able to share what the experience is like for me when I participate?

Co-regulation only works if you are in a better spot than your child or teen to begin with. On a scale of 1 to 10, with 1 being very calm and 10 being very distressed, you don't have to be at a Zen-like 1 to co-regulate well, but you need to be below a 7 in how distressed *you* are. **Remember: It's your cool brain that is going to regulate your child's hot one.**

The Magnifying Glass

In this body-scanning exercise, you can use a real or imaginary magnifying glass to pay extra-close attention to physical sensations. Young children in particular may enjoy moving—or pretending to move—a magnifying glass over their bodies. You might say, "Imagine you have a magnifying glass that allows you to see what's happening in your foot. What do you see?" You will be exchanging observations as you notice your own physical experiences too, beginning with both sets of feet planted on the ground. In this exercise, the caregiver starts out as both the guide and participant.

1. Begin by asking the child or teen whether he would prefer to sit or stand. Follow his lead. If he chooses to stand up, you might suggest that you lean against the wall together to conserve energy.

2. Once seated or standing, bring your attention to the part of your body that is touching the floor, and suggest that the child do the same. You could say something like "First, let's see if we can notice our feet on the ground."

3. Invite the child to take a few breaths, in through the nose and out through the mouth. At this time, you might briefly scan your own body, noting any sensations or emotions and seeing if you can also observe your own experience without judging it.

4. Facilitate the body scan. Continue to both model and encourage deeper breathing as, together, you slowly move upward, body section by body section, shifting your attention gradually from the bottom of your feet to the crown of your head.

5. As you guide the child, pay attention to your own body sensations, and use them to facilitate further inquiry. For example, you might say something like "I'm noticing some tightness in my left leg today. Do you notice some tightness too? Or do you feel something completely different?" or "Oh, that's interesting that you don't feel anything at all in your tummy. Mine is rumbling a little." Whatever we feel, it is good to notice—and it is likely to pass.

6. You can go through the magnifying glass activity slowly or quickly, depending on how engaged your child or teen seems. Younger kids and those who aren't extremely dysregulated may complete this whole scan in just a couple of minutes. Others who are more into the exploration, or who need more time to regroup, can engage for 10 minutes or even more.

Try to take cues from the child to determine when to bring the exercise to a close.

7. Check in at the end of the exercise to discuss how each of you is feeling now. First, ask your child or teen if he feels calmer, and then tell him how you're feeling now too. For example, you might say, "That was helpful for to me to realize how tense my shoulders felt. It helped to relax them."

8. Use this metric to gauge the effectiveness of the activity: "On a scale of 1 to 10, where 1 is very relaxed and 10 is how you felt before we did this activity, how are you feeling now?" Anything below a 7 is good. If your child is still at or over a 7, you might want to try using the magnifying glass again—or try something else that might help him become calmer.

Basic body parts to magnify and discuss (add as you and your child find interesting):

_____ **Bottom of the feet** (touching the ground—add if you like: top of feet, ankles)

_____ **Legs** (can add shins, calves, quads, hamstrings, knees)

_____ **Tummy** (can use other words, like stomach, belly, or middle, as feels comfortable)

_____ **Chest** (opening to let in the air and strength)

_____ **Back** (bottom, lower back, upper back)

_____ **Arms** (upper arms, lower arms, wrists)

_____ **Hands** (palm, fingers)

_____ **Neck** (shoulders)

_____ **Jaw/face** (temples, forehead)

_____ **Top of head** (reaching up to the sky)

Relaxing Muscles Together

In this exercise, you will do a full body scan, just as you did in the magnifying glass activity, but this time you will be actively squeezing and releasing your muscles at the same time. When working with a hypoactivated child, it might be useful to reflect your experiences out loud by saying what it feels like, for example, to clench your jaw or scrunch your toes. Doing so can increase connection between you and your child. You can ask—but don't insist on an answer—what the experience is like for your child as you progress upward through the body. In contrast, if you are working with a hyperactivated child and need to bring energy down, it might be better just to suggest what's next and to clench and release those muscle groups with relatively quiet focus.

1. Begin by asking the child or teen whether she prefers to sit or stand. Follow her lead. If she chooses to stand up, you might suggest that you lean against the wall together to conserve energy.

2. Once seated or standing, bring your attention to the part of your body that is touching the floor, and suggest that the child or teen do the same. (Whether you are seated in a chair or standing, you can begin by saying something like "Let's start by noticing our feet on the floor.")

3. Invite the child or teen to join you in taking a few breaths, in through the nose and out through the mouth. At this time, you might briefly do a preview scan of your own body, noting any sensations or emotions. Try to observe your experience without judging it.

4. Facilitate the body scan by inviting your child to continue breathing while you engage each of your muscle groups, and gradually move your awareness from your feet to your head (e.g., "Let's focus first on our left foot and squeeze all our left-foot muscles. Let's squeeze, squeeze, squeeze! Annnnnnd release").

5. The length of this activity will depend upon the child's age, developmental level, and capacity to tolerate any bodily sensations or emotions that arise. You should take cues from your child to determine when to bring the activity to a close.

6. The next time you practice this activity, see if the child or teen wants to facilitate instead of you. You might ask, "Do you want to relax our muscles together to get grounded? Do you want to lead the activity? I will follow your lead. Should we sit or stand?"

7. Check in at the end of the exercise to discuss how each of you is feeling now. First, ask your child if she feels calmer, and then tell her how you're feeling now too.

8. Use this metric to gauge the effectiveness of the activity: "On a scale of 1 to 10, where 1 is very relaxed and 10 is how you felt before we did this activity, how are you feeling now?" Anything below a 7 is good. If your child is still at or over a 7, you might want to practice this exercise one more time—or try something else that might help her become calmer.

Notice All Five Senses

This popular exercise, also known as the "5-4-3-2-1 Technique," is used to help dysregulated and stressed-out people of all ages. It's tried and true for supporting distressed and panicky kids in returning to the present moment and offers some immediate relief from symptoms. Of course, the variation presented here makes it into a relational activity for *both* of you to do together.

1. Begin by offering your child or teen a general overview of the task. Say something like "Let's play a calming game by exploring our five senses" (younger kids) or "Let's try to get more grounded together by exploring our five senses" (older children and teens). "You go first." Ask your child to tell you:

   - **Five things he can see** (then it's your turn)

   - **Four things he can touch** (then it's your turn)

   - **Three things he can hear** (then it's your turn)

   - **Two things he can smell** (then it's your turn)

   - **One thing he can taste (or would love to eat)** (then it's your turn)

2. Always have your child or teen go first for each sense—unless he'd prefer you to. Either way, your child will have the bonus experience of additional grounding when he hears what you notice. Don't worry about coming up with all unique responses, but remember that every time you name something new, it brings that sensation into your child's awareness too.

3. If the child or teen doesn't want to hear your ideas—or is too dysregulated to take turns—you might just offer him a mindful and compassionate presence, sitting with him as *he* counts down and becomes calmer.

4. When you have both counted down through your senses, ask the child if he feels calmer, and tell him how you're feeling now too.

5. Use the metric to gauge the effectiveness of the activity: "On a scale of 1 to 10, where 1 is very relaxed and 10 is how you felt before we did this activity, how are you feeling now?" Anything below a 7 is good. If your child is still at or over a 7, you might want to count down through the five senses again—or try something else that might help him become calmer.

Grounding Chairs—Time-Out for Two

This activity is really like a "time-out corner for two." The exercise stems from a significant body of research showing that traumatized, stressed-out kids experience being banished to time-out not as a chance to regroup but as terrifying, rejecting isolation. For kids who may need adult presence to calm down or to return to the present moment, the activity offers a co-regulating alternative to the traditional time-out approach.

1. Have a conversation with your child or teen at a calm time. Say you want to try something new when there is a stressful interaction or when you need to get back into simple connection after a busy day. Explain that you want to see "what it's like to have a time-out *together*."

2. Ask your child or teen to help you set up a cozy place in your home with two chairs. These chairs should be out of the main traffic pattern of the home. You may consider adding other calming elements as you go along, such as a couple of favorite stuffed animals, a scented candle, a little soft ball to pass back and forth, a weighted blanket big enough for two, or a picture of a peaceful scene. If you have a view outside your window, consider putting the chairs nearby to offer a calming distraction.

3. This corner is designated as a place where either of you can suggest taking a time-out *together*. Set a timer for a few minutes if that helps frame the activity, and see what it's like to quietly sit there. At the end of the time, check in. You are welcome to stay longer if anyone needs to, but it's a good idea to start off by planning to be there about five minutes and leaving soon after you are both a little calmer. You can decide along the way what is both tolerable and helpful, depending on how the activity is going. But remember: Time out isn't supposed to be aversive.

4. Although your goal might be to have your child initiate visits to the grounding chairs when she is upset, begin by making the invitation yourself whenever the situation is heating up or whenever the sense of disconnection becomes concerning to you.

5. In these circumstances, you can say, "Let's go sit quietly together and cool down. We won't do a lot of talking until we feel better, but we will be together."

6. Once seated, offer to take a few breaths together. Whether or not your child agrees to do so, you should take a few deep breaths, in through the nose and out through the mouth.

7. The conversation, if any, can begin with a focus on grounding your bodies. Notice what it feels like to sit in the chair.

8. It might help to begin by doing a body scan together, starting with the feet. Have your child or teen tap each part of her body as she notices how it feels, attending to the places where each body part is contacting another body part or touching the chair. Basic body parts to use during the body scan include:

   - **Bottom of the feet** (touching the ground—add if you like: top of feet, ankles)

   - **Legs** (can add shins, calves, quads, hamstrings, knees)

   - **Tummy** (can use other words, like stomach, belly, or middle, as feels comfortable)

   - **Chest** (opening to let in the air and strength)

   - **Back** (bottom, lower back, upper back)

   - **Arms** (upper arms, lower arms, wrists)

   - **Hands** (palm, fingers)

   - **Neck** (shoulders)

   - **Jaw/face** (temples, forehead)

   - **Top of head** (reaching up to the sky)

9. When you are ready to end the activity, ask your child if she feels calmer, and tell her how you're feeling now too.

10. Use the metric to gauge the effectiveness of the activity: "On a scale of 1 to 10, where 1 is very relaxed and 10 is how you felt before we did this activity, how are you feeling now?" Anything below a 7 is good. If your child is still at or over a 7, you might want to sit a little longer or to do a body scan if you haven't already tried that—or suggest something else that might help her become calmer.

Going Out and Going In

The focus of our attention in grounding exercises is always toward the present moment. We want to notice what is happening "right here and right now"—both internally and externally. In this activity, you'll move attention from **going out into the room**, to **going into the body experience**, and then **back outward into the relationship**.

In this exercise, "going out" orients us to the world around us. It is a calming way to engage with what is happening in our external environment. In balance, "going in" orients us to ourselves. When we turn to our internal experiences, we notice our thoughts, feelings, and sensations to relax our bodies and minds. After we spend time becoming aware of ourselves and our surroundings, we are freshly able to connect with others. Therefore, this exercise concludes by having you and your child focus attention once again toward each other. This is a potential way to establish a grounding re-connection between you and your child, whether it's through a shared warm gaze or—if it's comfortable to do so—a good regulating hug.

Going Out

1. Begin by inviting the child to breathe with you and to notice the points of contact between your bodies and your seats and the floor.

2. You might say, "Let's first focus on being right here, right now by looking for things that are in the room."

3. Take turns for a round or two seeing how many things you can each find in the room that meet a certain description. You might identify objects, sounds, textures, colors, smells, shapes, or numbers. For example, ask your child or teen:

   - Can you name three square things?

   - Can you find two blue things?

   - Can you identify five things that are smaller than a shoebox?

   - Two smelly things?

   - Three soft things?

4. You can do this as a guessing game too—like "I Spy with My Little Eye"—where you follow each other's attention. For example, take turns seeing if the other person can find what you have hinted at:

   • How many things in this room have legs?

   • Guess which picture on the wall is my favorite.

   • I see five shiny objects. Can you find them?

   • I spy with my little eye something blue and striped. What is it?

5. Check in by asking, "On a scale of 1 to 10, where 1 is perfectly calm and 10 is the way you felt when we began, how are you feeling now?" Share your experience of the activity. For example, you could say, "I had a lot of fun when you gave me great clues. I feel much more relaxed now. I'm at a 5, and I was at an 8 when we began. Wow!"

6. Suggest that you might both enjoy **going in** to help you continue to calm down even further.

Going In

1. Invite the child or teen to close his eyes or to gaze gently at one object on the ceiling or floor.

2. Engage your child in a body scan, beginning at the feet and progressing to the top of the head.

3. In this variation, you might want to encourage your child to notice his thoughts, emotions, and body sensations throughout, sharing your own curious experience of the activity. For example:

   • "When you feel your feet on the ground, what thoughts do you have? It is interesting, I'm thinking that I'd like to wiggle my toes." (Thought)

   • "I'm thinking about how hard it can be to settle my mind. I'm glad I have you to practice with." (Thought)

   • "How does it feel to sit quietly with me? Is it comforting for you too?" (Feeling)

   • "Do you notice that you are feeling calmer than before we sat down?" (Feeling)

   • "When I push down on my heels, I notice that they tingle a little. What's that like for you?" (Sensation)

- "I was feeling relaxed until I got to my chest. It's still kind of tight. I think I need to take a couple more breaths. Can you help me with that?" (Sensation)

Back Out into the Relationship

1. Invite the child or teen to look at you. Return his gaze with a warm smile.

2. Say something like "I'm glad we did this together. I'm calmer now. How about you?"

3. Recognize the effort it took to do this exercise, and notice the change in thoughts, emotions, and body sensations that led to a greater sense of calm and connection.

When you are ready to end the activity, ask your child or teen if he feels calmer, and tell him how you're feeling now too. Use this metric to gauge the effectiveness of the activity: "On a scale of 1 to 10, where 1 is very relaxed and 10 is how you felt before we did this activity, how are you feeling now?" Anything below a 7 is good. If your child is still at or over a 7, you might want to ask him if he'd like to do the activity another time—or one of you could suggest something else that might help him feel better regulated and more connected.

Be a Tree

The idea of grounding—planting our feet solidly into the ground, feeling rooted, and standing strong—readily evokes the image of a sturdy tree that won't get blown over or swept away by overwhelming feelings. In this activity and its variations, you and your child will become two solid trees, going through the following steps together.

The Basic Tree Exercise

1. Suggest to your child that you would like to "try imagining that we are both trees."

2. Stand with your feet parallel and at least shoulder-width apart. Keep your heads floating above your bodies, your gaze straight ahead, and your spines straight, the way a strong, rooted tree might appear. (If anyone can't stand, sitting will work too.)

3. Offer some details, beginning with your feet:

    - Feel your feet planted on the ground.

    - Imagine long roots growing from the bottoms of your feet deep into the earth.

    - Imagine that your backs are the trunks.

    - Imagine that your arms are sturdy branches.

4. To bring awareness to your tree-bodies, try squeezing your muscles, group by group, as tightly as you can and holding them like that for a moment.

    - Clench your toes, leg muscles, buttocks, stomachs, fists, and even faces.

    - Take a deep breath, hold it, and then let it all out with a big exhale, imagining all this energy you were hanging onto is flowing out of your bodies, down through your roots, and into the earth.

5. Shake all over: Shake any of your excess energy out through our arms and hands, like branches blowing in the wind.

6. Repeat this exercise three times or until both of you feel calmer.

A Big Wind in the Branches

1. If either of you can think of something in particular that has upset you or made you feel angry, you can imagine this anger, worry, or pain as though it is the wind blowing through the branches. Stretch your arms high, with your hands wide open.

2. Take those upsetting or angry thoughts, and imagine balling them up in your hands.

3. Clench your hands, and with a deep inhale, lift your clenched hands up high above your head into the imaginary wind, and with a big, long exhale, drop your hands down and "throw" this anger into the earth.

4. Once again, shake this excess energy out of your arms and hands.

5. Repeat this several times until neither of you feel so angry or upset.

6. For the final time, do it very slowly and deliberately.

7. Notice now: When the wind comes, does your body feel strong? If you feel like the wind can still push your body around, then add a bigger root system to your feet. Imagine that you have many roots holding you firmly to the ground. Feel how great it is to be so solidly connected to the earth and how strong your body feels.

A More Peaceful Tree

1. You can also simply imagine yourselves with a trunk and tree roots reaching down into the earth.

2. Whenever you feel insecure, scared, nervous, or anxious, you can imagine that all your worries are flowing down your trunk, through your roots, and into the earth where it generates new energy.

3. Or you can reach up to the sky—imagining that your arms are branches—and open your hands, letting the imaginary wind just gently carry your hard feelings away.

4. You can use this exercise to gently stretch together when your child looks like she's starting to wind up. Plant your feet, reach up to the sky, and invite her to sway and breathe together with you for a minute. Let the worries flow into the ground and away with the wind.

Check in at the end of all of these tree variations by asking, "How do you feel now? Are you grounded and feeling calmer?" Share your own experience with your child or teen. For example, you might say something like "I noticed that when I pushed my feet into the ground, it really felt like I had roots!"

Use this metric to gauge the effectiveness of the activity: "On a scale of 1 to 10, where 1 is very relaxed and 10 is how you felt before we did this activity, how are you feeling now?" Anything below a 7 is good. If your child is still at or over a 7, you might want to try one of the tree variations another time—or think together if there is something else you might do with each other that might feel more grounding.

Happy Feet

This activity encourages exploration of an often overlooked and underappreciated body part that is very helpful in keeping us standing strong: our feet. Unless they are receiving a pedicure, having a massage, or visiting a podiatrist, most people don't take the time to attend to and to appreciate the amazing appendages that support them. It's worth noting that dysregulated kids can struggle with balance and coordination, and increasing awareness of their feet can be a useful first step in increasing overall body awareness. Paying attention to our feet can be calming and (literally) grounding. In this exercise, you and your child will focus together on all four of the available happy feet: heels, arches, pads, *and* everyone's funny toes.

1. Invite the child or teen to remove his shoes and socks as you do the same.

2. Begin with a foot examination from heel to toe. This can be done visually through light touch or gentle squeezing.

3. Then you can really get into the study, for example, by:

   • Counting the bones in the toes

   • Comparing your feet, toe by toe

   • Examining the toenails, bumps, callouses, and shapes of the different toes

   • Looking at your arches change shape as you flex and point your toes

   • Getting a piece of paper and pencil and tracing the outlines of your feet

   • Talking about how the pencil feels as it moves around your feet. Does it tickle?

   • Smoothing your toenails with an emery board

   • Painting your toenails (or drawing toenails on the foot outline you made and coloring those in)

   • Looking up the skeleton of a foot on the internet and studying how the bones all fit together

   • Having a warm foot bath or massaging your own feet with lotion or oil, paying attention to the sensory experience of it all—and comparing notes

4. Next, walk barefoot across different surfaces inside or even outside to feel the different sensations on the bottom of your feet. What does it feel like to walk barefoot on carpet, tile, pavement, grass, and so on?

5. Rock back and forth on your bare feet—waking them up—heel-toe, heel-toe, heel-toe.

6. Stand on barefoot tippy toes, and see how long you can keep your balance. Can you shut your eyes for a couple moments without falling over?

7. Hop, skip, jump, or shuffle together while barefoot, trying to match the rhythm and intensity of your child's movement.

8. Walk on your hands and feet like an animal in the forest.

9. Check in at the end of the activity by asking, "How do you feel now? Are you grounded and feeling calmer?" Share what the experience was like for you. For example, "My feet feel much happier now that I have taken good care of them. I feel more grounded knowing I have paid attention to them and to you!"

10. Use this metric to gauge the effectiveness of the activity: "On a scale of 1 to 10, where 1 is very relaxed and 10 is how you felt before we did this activity, how are you feeling now?" Anything below a 7 is good. If your child is still at or over a 7, you might want to try some more happy feet variations—or consider whether there is something else you might do together to help with co-regulation.

Drawing Music

Listening to music can, in itself, be grounding, but this activity adds touch, sight, and co-regulation to the calming mix. Before trying this exercise, pick a piece of music that you and your child or teen both like listening to. It doesn't have to be a calm song—but all the better if you can find one that doesn't leave anyone's head throbbing. You will be drawing how the music makes you feel by creating a dancing line with a pencil and paper.

1. Sit side by side at a table, making sure each of you has a piece of paper and something to draw with.

2. When the song begins, start drawing a line as the music plays, representing on the page what you hear.

3. Follow the music with the pencil, watching your hand flow along with the song.

4. When the music is over, compare your drawings, and notice the ways in which they are the same and different. Be sure to compliment any effort that your child or teen has put forth. If your child focused on the task, that means he was actively engaged in grounding with you!

5. If you so desire, listen to the song again, perhaps this time sharing the same blank page with your child and drawing above each other so you move in parallel. Maybe one of you could listen to the vocal part and another to the guitar (or you might attend to different instruments). When the song ends, see how your lines follow similar and different patterns and how they work together.

6. If there are loops and patterns, color them in as you listen yet another time.

7. When you are finished coloring, check in and use this metric to gauge the effectiveness of the activity: "On a scale of 1 to 10, where 1 is very relaxed and 10 is how you felt before we did this activity, how are you feeling now?" Anything below a 7 is good. If your child is still at or over a 7 but heading in the right direction, you might want to try this activity a bit longer by listening to a new song, using more improvisational scribbling instead of a single line, or changing it up by drawing the music with your non-dominant hand or both hands at once. You can make up your own variations. Just put on your favorite song, sit down together with some colored pencils, and see what happens next.

Push on the Wall

This activity offers hyperactivated kids an opportunity to discharge excess energy in a safe and playful manner. It literally provides exercise and offers grounding input into muscles and joints throughout the body. As you and your child push together with all of your might on an immovable object—the wall—you can turn an escalating confrontation into a shared endeavor to get some energy out.

1. Invite your child or teen to stand beside you facing a sturdy, plain wall.

2. Place your palms on the wall, and press into it utilizing your entire body weight. Say, "Let's try and feel more grounded by pushing hard on this wall. Can you try it with me? Maybe we can even push the wall over!" (Note: You know your child—if the thought of a wall falling over would be upsetting, don't go that far in this invitation.)

3. Once your child understands what to do, encourage her to join you if she hasn't already done so: "It might feel good to push hard on something really strong right now. Let's see if we can push it for 10 seconds! Let's count."

4. Push three times on the wall for 10 seconds each time.

5. Breathe deeply between exertions.

6. Experiment with walking toward and away from the wall while maintaining considerable pressure with your hands. Try pushing with one foot in front of the other, with both feet next to each other, with your legs bent, and with your legs straight. Keep pushing no matter how you move the rest of your legs and body.

7. Do a couple of wall push-ups, feeling your arm muscles contract and lengthen.

8. You can also try pushing against the wall with your backs for a count of 10, with your legs splayed out or in a squatting position.

9. Share your body experience with your child or teen. For example, you might say something like "My hands are sweaty and my knees feel stiff. Did you notice some tightness in your knees too?" or "This wall is lumpy (or slippery, cold, etc.) on my palms. What is it like for you?"

10. If this activity works well, you might consider tracing and cutting out your handprints on card stock paper and having them laminated. Then you can put the prints on the wall in fun poses for you to push against. These decorations will serve as handy visual reminders of a grounding activity you can use the next time the roller coaster takes off.

11. Talk about the experience afterward. Make sure to ask how your child is feeling, and briefly describe how the activity felt to you too: "I am really tired now. It felt good to get all that energy out on the wall."

12. Use this metric to gauge the effectiveness of the exercise: "On a scale of 1 to 10, where 1 is very relaxed and 10 is how you felt before we did this activity, how are you feeling now?" Anything below a 7 is good. If your child is still at or over a 7, you might want to try to this exercise a while longer—or consider if there is something else you might do together that might help her become calmer.

SOS: Slow Down, Orient, Self-Check

SOS is a grounding technique to help children and teens feel in more control in the present moment. In SOS, you will go slowly through three steps that will enable both of you to focus better, to think more clearly, to feel closer, to have fewer overwhelming feelings, and to reset your energy all in just a few minutes.

1. **Slow down:** Say, "SOS! We need help! First, let's try to *slow down*. Let's sit back and take a few deep breaths together." Pay attention to your breathing, and try to sync it up with your child's breathing to slow both of you down. Talk calmly, and try to have just one thought at a time. Think only about slowing down and breathing, breathing and slowing down.

2. **Orient:** Say, "Let's get *oriented* to the here and now. Where are we? Who is here? What time of day is it? What day of the week is it? What are we doing right now? Are our feet planted firmly on the floor? Let's look at each other and smile just because we are here together and we can."

3. **Self-check:** Use this metric to do a *self-check* and to gauge the effectiveness of the exercise: "On a scale of 1 to 10, where 1 is very relaxed and 10 is how you felt before we did this activity, how are you feeling now?" Anything below a 7 is good. If your child is still at or over a 7, you might want to go back to the start and practice the *slow down* step together some more. You can also orient further by using **The Five Senses** or the **Going In, Going Out** strategies presented earlier in this chapter. Finally, consider whether there is another activity you can do together that would help lower stress levels and increase co-regulation—and then try SOS again afterward for good measure.

---

* Based on the work of Julian Ford (2006) in *Trauma-focused, present-centered, emotional self-regulation approach to integrated treatment for posttraumatic stress and addiction.*

6

Breathing Together

Mindful breathing is an established, emotionally regulating practice that has helped people feel centered for thousands of years. Research has demonstrated that breathing *with* your child or teen also confers real benefits for your relationship. In this chapter, you will learn about and practice breathing as an effective strategy for co-regulation. When you and your child breathe together, you both will feel closer and calmer. And there's a bonus: If you can model steady, even breathing, you will discover that your child's breathing patterns will actually slow to match your own with ongoing practice. Just as fear and activation are contagious, so is slow, intentional inhaling and exhaling.

It's advisable to begin by teaching and practicing these 12 breathing strategies when you and your child are relatively calm so you can both get comfortable with the exercises. It's likely that if you spring a new suggestion on a child in the middle of a meltdown, it will not be well received. But if he knows what to do and has some positive earlier experiences breathing with you, he'll be more likely to give breathing a try when it is needed most.

Breathing with your kids in stressful circumstances lets them know you are still there even when they are falling apart, especially since trying to engage in a conversation with your child can make things worse in these situations. When you take a deep breath, you are also putting the brakes on your own reactivity. You can then acknowledge that your child is having a hard time by saying something along the lines of, "That was really frustrating when you had to come inside for dinner before you were done riding your scooter." Then suggest that you and your child experiment with one of the exercises you previously practiced that was effective. Afterward, check in about whether the activity was helpful and whether either of you are feeling better as a consequence. Easily dysregulated kids need plenty of support noticing the difference in their bodies when they are feeling calm versus distressed. Ideally, breathing together will help your child learn how to recognize and move between these very different states of being.

For each activity presented in this chapter, it is important to consider the following points:

- Always do the breathing activity alongside your child. Maximum benefits come when the breathing activity is shared. This also means staying sufficiently close to your child so he can feel your presence and support.
- It is not essential, but try to find a quiet space to sit, stand, or lie down to complete the breathing exercises. These activities don't work as well if you are multitasking.

If you are at the sink doing dishes when you start sensing trouble, turn around and take a few steps away from the chore to become more fully present.

- Even though breathing helps us calm down and be peaceful, it doesn't mean breathing has to be so serious. If you and your child are not in an epic struggle, bring a sense of playfulness and lightheartedness to the breathing exercises—make them fun. You also don't need to do these activities perfectly to benefit from them.

- Breathing exercises gain power with repetition and practice. You may start off breathing through just one cycle of inhalations and exhalations, but over time, you will notice that you can breathe together longer and with more relaxing benefits.

Back-to-Back Breathing

If you and your child are comfortable with touch, this activity can offer an easy way to breathe together. Breathing back to back invites you and your child to co-regulate through physical contact *and* awareness of breath. It creates feelings of calm and connection.

1. Begin by sitting back to back with your backs nice and tall. You can be sitting in any position that feels most comfortable to you. Many feel supported sitting cross-legged or with their legs straight in front of them.

2. Close your eyes, or let them rest on one point in front of you. Notice what it feels like to touch backs, and just relax into the support. Enjoy being here together.

3. Take a few easy breaths on your own, letting your breath gently flow in and out.

4. Decide who will start. This person—known as the leading partner—begins by inhaling deeply and then exhaling slowly, and then continues to breathe slowly and deeply.

5. The following partner should feel the leading partner's back expand with each in-breath. The goal is to try to synchronize your breathing so both of you are breathing in time together.

6. Switch roles. By the end of the exercise, both you and your child should have had the chance to lead and to follow.

7. Talk about the experience afterward. Make sure to ask how your child is feeling, and briefly describe how the activity felt to you too: "I loved it when you were the leader. It felt good to calm down together."

Bunny Breathing

You don't have to get down on the floor and act like a bunny to do this exercise (though it will be more fun if you do!). Bunny breathing also works fine in a sitting or standing position if being on the floor is hard for you for any reason. This activity has a couple of goals. The first is to give you and your child the simple pleasure of pretending together. How often do you get to play like bunnies? A more serious goal is to help your anxious child identify the difference between short and long breaths. Bunny breathing will help your child understand how to slow down his breathing on his own when he starts getting worked up about something.

1. Sit next to each other on the floor on your shins—leaning forward, with your backs straight—like bunnies.

2. Explain to your child that you will both be pretending to be bunnies sniffing the air for other bunnies to play with or for carrots to eat.

3. Model taking three quick sniffs in through the nose and one long exhalation out of the nose.

4. Repeat this sequence several times: sniff, sniff, sniff, b-r-e-a-t-h-e. Sniff, sniff, sniff for carrots, and then breathe out slowly. Sniff, sniff, sniff for flowers, and then breathe out slowly. Sniff, sniff, sniff for berries, and then breathe out slowly.

5. Help your child notice the difference between long and short breaths. Try to make the long breaths even longer as you practice this exercise.

6. Talk about the experience afterward. Make sure to ask how your child is feeling, and briefly describe how the activity felt to you too: "I liked being a bunny with you. It was fun to sniff for carrots and then breathe ouuuuuuut."

Humming Bee Breathing

Humming bee breathing is a technique used in yoga that has proven to be effective in calming the mind down quickly. It can be useful for reducing agitation, frustration, and anxiety. Some people say that it helps them feel less angry too. In this version, you will take turns practicing and doing the activity together.

1. Sit in chairs or on the floor, with your backs straight, facing each other.

2. Take turns closing your eyes—if this feels comfortable to do—and plugging your ears with your index fingers. (You don't have to put your fingers inside your ears. Pressing gently on the cartilage between your ear and cheek works very well.)

3. Inhale through your nose, and quietly hum the "mmm" sound as you exhale, sounding like a bee.

4. You will feel vibrations in your head, calming the nervous system.

5. When you are done with a big humming exhale, open your eyes, and tell your child or teen it is his turn.

6. Go back and forth for three or four rounds. You can keep going if it's fun and helpful.

7. Decide whether it feels more calming if you hum high or low, or even high *and* low, in the course of an exhale. Feel free to try different sounds to see if they help too!

8. Take the time between turns to make eye contact and smile warmly. This connection in itself is calming.

9. Talk about the experience afterward. Make sure to ask how your child is feeling, and briefly describe how the activity felt to you too: "I am much calmer now. Those vibrations really helped me feel less worried."

Roaring Lion Breathing

This breathing exercise can turn an escalating conflict into a more playful discharge of emotion. Younger children particularly enjoy this exercise because they can make a lot of noise and don't have to "use their words" to communicate big feelings. Best of all, because it is a shared activity, you get to do some roaring too. Like the other pretend animal exercises, this one is designed for both you and your child to kneel on the floor, but it works just fine from sitting or standing positions too.

1. Facing each other, kneel together on the floor with your bottoms resting on your calves, or sit cross-legged.

2. Place your hands on your knees, and sit up straight.

3. Take a big inhale, and then open your mouth wide, wrinkle your nose, and make the biggest possible "ROARRRR!" sound on the exhale. Then smile and tell your child it is her turn. After she has roared, it is your turn again.

4. Do this a few times, and then try to end with a big simultaneous "ROAR!" together.

5. Talk about the experience afterward. Make sure to ask how your child is feeling, and briefly describe how the activity felt to you too: "Wow, we can really roar when we try! I'm so relaxed, I'm ready for a big cat nap!"

High Fives Breathing

High fives breathing connects the breath to a simple hand gesture. When you and your child do this exercise together, you will be synchronizing your breathing and hand movements. Sometimes it is hard to stay focused on a breathing task for relaxation. We find that our minds start racing, we lose track of what we are doing, and we may have difficulty completing the task. For an added element of grounding, this exercise uses touch to help focus our attention and keep us engaged.

1. Sit comfortably in chairs or on the floor facing each other.

2. Extend one hand in front of you with your fingers outstretched, like a star. Have your child make the mirror image of this so your hands are facing each other but not touching.

3. Take the pointer finger of your other hand, and place it on the base of your thumb of your outstretched hand. Make sure your child continues to mirror all you are doing.

4. Together with your child, slowly breathe in through your nose as you slide your pointer finger up to the top of your thumb.

5. Now slowly breathe out, and slide your finger down the inside of your thumb.

6. Breathe in as you slide your finger up the next finger, and breathe out as you slide down.

7. Try to remain in sync with a slow pace of inhaling, exhaling, and moving your pointer finger along each digit.

8. Don't speed up. Keep steady and in sync as you breathe in and out and trace your whole hand.

9. Change directions, together slowly returning back to the outside of your thumbs.

10. If you are comfortable, try tracing each other's hands as you stay aware of the other person's pace of breathing.

11. Talk about the experience afterward. Make sure to ask how your child is feeling, and briefly describe how the activity felt to you too: "It was hard to do this slowly, but we really got in sync with our breathing by the time we got back to the thumb!"

Elephant Breathing

Elephant breathing is helpful for kids who start shutting down when they feel overwhelmed. In this exercise, the motions don't require great effort but still get your child breathing deeply. When you engage in elephant breathing, you can feel like a parent and child elephant moving together through the jungle. Use your imagination to wake up the body gently, and coordinate your movements naturally.

1. Stand next to each other, with your feet spread wide apart, making sure there is enough room to swing your arms up and down.

2. Dangle your head and arms in front of you. Clasp your dangling hands to turn your arms into an elephant trunk.

3. Breathe in through your nose as you slowly swing your arms above your head.

4. Then breathe out through your mouth as you slowly swing your arms back down.

5. Repeat this movement three times.

6. Try moving slowly together across the room as you swing your trunks in unison.

7. Talk about the experience afterward. Make sure to ask how your child is feeling, and briefly describe how the activity felt to you too: "I liked being your relaxed mama elephant. I hope we can roam the savannah together again tomorrow."

A more energized variation of this exercise is called Woodchopper Breathing. Instead of having your hands and arms serve as a lazy elephant trunk, imagine you are chopping firewood with an ax. Raise the ax way above your head on the inhale, and with a vigorous exhale, make a "HAA" sound as you quickly lower your hands, holding the imaginary ax all the way to the floor. Think about chopping away anger, fear, or negativity. Do this a few times together and discuss how it felt.

Shoulder Breathing

Distress causes us to breathe with short, shallow breaths from our chest instead of breathing with long, deep breaths from our belly. Shoulder breathing ensures that you'll expand your lungs enough to feel the full benefit of a long, relaxing inhale and exhale.

1. Sit in chairs comfortably across from each other. (You can also stand facing each other if you prefer.)

2. As you take a slow, deep breath in through your nose, raise your shoulders up toward your ears.

3. Then slowly breathe out through your mouth, lowering your shoulders as you exhale.

4. Repeat slowly, in a continuous movement of shoulder rolls timed with the breath.

5. You can put your hands on your shoulders (or on each other's shoulders) to feel the full motion accompanying the inhale and exhale.

6. Repeat until you both feel a little more relaxed and calmer—at least three times.

7. Talk about the experience afterward. Make sure to ask how your child is feeling, and briefly describe how the activity felt to you too: "I feel less stressed now. It felt good to breathe deeply."

Calming Count Breathing

Calming count breathing is a simple slow-things-down exercise that makes the most of a frustrating situation. Instead of just counting to 10 so you don't blow a gasket, invite your child to count to 10 *and* to breathe together with you. When you get to 10, do the same counting and breathing backward to 1. That's it! Though it can be challenging to count while inhaling, it might just calm you both down and get things back on track.

1. Breathe in, ONE

2. Exhale, TWO

3. Inhale, THREE

4. Exhale, FOUR

5. Inhale, FIVE

6. Exhale, SIX

7. Inhale, SEVEN

8. Exhale, EIGHT

9. Inhale, NINE

10. Exhale, TEN

11. Inhale NINE... (continue to count backward to the beginning)

12. Talk about the experience afterward. Make sure to ask how your child is feeling, and briefly describe how the activity felt to you too: "Breathing together with you really helps me calm down. I started feeling a little less stressed on the way up, but when we got back to 5, I was pretty mellow."

Triangle Breathing

There are many ways to use different shapes to help you visualize breathing with your child or teen. Triangle breathing is perhaps the simplest, but if you want to experiment with squares, pentagons, stars, or even octagons, it's all good. Just follow this three-part strategy: Breathe in, hold your breath, and breathe out—each in an equal measure of time. Get two pieces of paper and a pen or pencil so you can draw the triangle (or any other shape) that you'll be following with your breath.

1. Each of you can draw a picture of a triangle, or have one to share.

2. Start by placing your finger at the bottom left corner of the triangle.

3. Together, breathe in for three counts as you trace the first side of the triangle.

4. Hold your breath for three counts as you trace the second side of the triangle.

5. Try to be aware of the pace: Keep it slow, steady, and in sync with each other.

6. Breathe out for three counts as you trace the final side of the triangle.

7. You have just completed one deep breath. Take the journey three times together.

8. Talk about the experience afterward. Make sure to ask how your child is feeling, and briefly describe how the activity felt to you too: "It helps me to breathe in sync with you when we trace the triangles. I feel more relaxed than I did before."

Relaxing Breath

Relaxing breathing follows a different breathing pattern than the previous exercises. You will inhale for a count of four, hold your breath for a count of seven, and exhale for a count of eight. This pattern (4:7:8 to inhale: hold: exhale) has researched calming benefits. If you are having difficulty holding your breath for seven counts, you can count faster. Eventually, as you build more deep breathing skills, you and your child should be able to slow down the practice. Take turns and then try it together.

1. Inhale gently through your nose while your partner counts to four.

2. Hold your breath for a count of seven.

3. Gently exhale your breath as your partner counts to eight.

4. You may enjoy trying "ocean breathing" as you exhale. Breathe out through the back of your throat. As you breathe out, go "ahhhhhh" as if you were fogging up a mirror. Notice the slight constriction at the back of your throat that creates the ocean sound. Ocean breathing slows the breath, focuses the mind, and offers the calming association of being by the sea.

5. Take turns breathing through the cycle of inhaling, holding, and exhaling four to six times or until you and your child feel a sense of calmness.

6. Then, if you feel like it, try synching up your relaxing breathing by doing it at the same time. You can count together on your fingers as you do the exercise.

7. Talk about the experience afterward. Make sure to ask how your child is feeling, and briefly describe how the activity felt to you too: "It really helped me to feel more peaceful when we did the ocean breathing together."

Belly Breathing

Belly breathing is a deep breathing technique that reduces fight-or-flight responses in the nervous system. When we breathe normally, we tend to inhale air into our chest. With belly breathing, we practice filling our bellies with air to reduce stress and relax. Since we are so used to chest breathing, this breathing activity may feel a little uncomfortable at first. Take your time!

1. Place your right hand over your heart and your left hand over your lower belly.

2. Inhale slowly through your nose as you gently fill your lower belly with air. Feel your hand on your belly and chest rise.

3. When your belly feels about 80 percent full, pause.

4. Release your breath, pulling in your lower belly, and feel your hand on your belly and chest fall.

5. Do this for a minute, and aim for just six full breaths in that time. Research suggests that the ratio of six breaths a minute offers optimal relaxation benefits from the exercise. If you can't slow your breathing down that much, no worries.

6. If you'd like to practice this activity while lying down, you could place special objects, like a stuffed animal or a small stone, on your bellies so you can see and feel the movement more clearly. Take turns, having your partner watch as your stuffed animal has a nice ride, rising and falling gently with the breath.

7. Talk about the experience afterward. Make sure to ask how your child is feeling, and briefly describe how the activity felt to you too: "I had no idea a minute was that long. It will take some practice to slow my breathing that much. But I do feel better than when we began!"

Loving-Kindness Breathing

When we are upset with ourselves, with other people, and with the situation we are in, our breathing mirrors our feelings of stress and our sense of being out of control. In alignment, our accompanying thoughts are usually unkind and unproductive. Distressed breathing and ungenerous thinking tend to go together. In contrast, loving-kindness breathing involves deeply inhaling compassionate thoughts to help you and your child both feel more centered and at peace. If your child or teen is too mad at you to extend compassion your way, he can still engage in this breathing exercise by thinking more compassionately about himself.

1. Sit comfortably across from each other.

2. Orient your attention to your body and emotions, and start slowing down your breathing together.

3. With younger children, put your arms around yourself, and ask them to do the same: "Let's give ourselves big hugs."

4. In unison, inhale deeply, and on the exhale, say this statement out loud:

   May I be safe.

5. Inhale deeply, and on the exhale, say this statement out loud:

   May I be peaceful.

6. Inhale deeply, and on the exhale, say this statement out loud:

   May I be kind to myself.

7. Inhale deeply, and on the exhale, say this statement out loud:

   May I accept myself as I am.

8. If you and your child are at an emotional place where you are willing to try sharing loving-kindness, use this same script and breathing pattern to look directly at each other while speaking these kind and compassionate statements:

   May you be safe.

   May you be peaceful.

   May you be kind to yourself.

   May I accept you as you are.

9. Discuss how it feels to extend loving-kindness to yourselves and to each other. It often leads to a nice sense of calm and peacefulness.

10. Ask if there is anyone else (or even the school, town, country, planet, or universe) to whom your child would like to offer this loving-kindness breathing. And of course: Do it together!

11. Talk about the experience afterward. Make sure to ask how your child is feeling, and briefly describe how the activity felt to you too: "I was really glad when you wanted to send loving-kindness to Grandpa. That felt extra good."

7

Creating Together

Once kids learn how to calm down, they need lots of practice staying in the regulated zone. The more time they have with that brain-healing experience of feeling cool, calm, and connected, the sturdier their platform for handling the frustrations and disappointments of life. Since most distressed children and adolescents don't want to engage in a lot of verbal processing, it helps to have some other hands-on ways to develop self-awareness. Cooperative, creative projects can be just the ticket. This chapter offers suggestions for crafty activities that kids and adults can do together. You'll see that the suggestions here have a slight therapeutic angle to them in that they might stimulate a conversation without "feelings talk" being the central purpose. Reflection can flow out of the shared activity rather than trying—yet again—to go through an unproductive rehashing of the hard times.

These ideas can be modified to fit what you both feel up to. You can figure out together how much time you want to spend on a particular project, how involved you'd like the product to be, and what kinds of play and discussions happen alongside it. Sometimes kids and their adults are both ready to roll up their sleeves and get messy. At other times, one person may want to keep it neat. This chapter offers an array of activities designed to resonate with both budding artists and people who like to follow more structured instructions.

My major recommendation is that you commit to a certain amount of time so you can be present and regulated yourself. It will defeat the purpose if you are impatient and try to quickly finish the activity just to be done with it. Hands-on projects can be enjoyable and exciting, and they offer the added benefit of co-regulation when you do them together. In this way, the process is every bit as important as the product—probably more so.

This chapter includes three kinds of projects: therapeutic art activities, creative games, and identity-building crafts. Each activity includes its suggested age range so you have the best chance of sharing in the effort—and so you won't end up stranded and doing it entirely yourself!

Mindful Breathing Wand*
Ages 4–7

This is another breathing exercise wrapped up in a fun art project. It requires a little adult supervision but is easy enough to keep frustration levels low. If you do the project slowly, by the time you've made the wand, you may both be feeling calm already. The mindful breathing wand will help you notice your breath and be expressive in the process.

Materials:

- Toilet roll or paper towel roll

- Markers

- Decorative items (e.g., stickers, glitter, buttons)

- Lightweight streamers or thin ribbon that can be moved with the breath

- Tape and glue

Instructions:

1. Cut off a one-inch piece from the toilet roll or paper towel roll, and set it aside for later use.

2. Cut a straight line all the way up the remainder of the roll.

3. Tighten the roll into a thinner roll, and use tape to secure it. That's the wand part.

4. Decorate the wand with markers and other decorative items. Get creative, but remember that this will be the stem of the wand that you hold.

5. Take the one-inch piece you set aside, and tape strands of lightweight ribbon or streamers along the inside.

6. Tape the one-inch piece on top of the decorated stem to make the flowy top of the wand.

---

* Adapted from https://kristinamarcelli.wordpress.com/2014/05/10/make-your-own-mindful-breathing-wand

7. That's it!

8. Inhale deeply, and breathe through the wand to make the streamers float in the air!

Some helpful questions to consider when you breathe through the breathing wand:

1. Take a breath in through your nose and blow out through your mouth. How do the streamers move?

2. What happens if you breathe really lightly into the wand? What about if you take a deep breath?

3. How do you feel breathing through the wand?

4. Pretend that the wand really has magical powers and could grant you three wishes. Inhale deeply, and blow through it three times, each time saying a wish.

5. Wave the wand slowly, and watch the ribbons flow in the wind. Can you sway together like the ribbons and relax like you are moving the same way in a gentle breeze?

6. How did it feel to each of you to make a wand and to play together with it?

7. What was the hardest part of the activity? What was the most fun for each of you?

Anger Volcano[*]
Ages 4–10

When we feel angry, our angry feelings sometimes erupt like a volcano! The anger volcano serves as an interesting and useful metaphor for helping children understand and develop a vocabulary to describe their powerful emotions. It's best if you do this activity when you and your child are feeling calm instead of waiting for your feelings to erupt.

Materials:

- Templates for the anger volcano and erupting lava (see next page)

- Glue

- Markers

Instructions:

1. Color the anger volcano template any color you'd like. Older children might like to color different levels of the volcano itself—making the bottom of the volcano represent a feeling of "calm" and the top of the volcano represent an "angry eruption."

2. Color the erupting lava fiery hot colors.

3. Cut out the anger volcano and erupting lava templates.

4. Place glue on the "glue here" tab, and glue the short ends of the anger volcano together.

5. Cut along the dotted lines on the erupting lava template to make tabs for lava, making sure not to cut all the way through.

6. Have a conversation about what makes each of you feel angry. What makes you erupt like a volcano? Write each of those things on the lava tabs. You can take turns sharing. It's good for your child to know you are working to manage your anger too.

   - Remember, now is a time to listen and to validate each other's feelings—not to get angry talking about it!

---

[*] Adapted from https://www.justonenorfolk.nhs.uk/media/1596/anger-activity.pdf

7. Fold the lava tabs along the dotted lines, and push it up through the hole from the bottom of the volcano. See your volcano erupting with the things that make you angry!

Some helpful phrases when you are discussing anger include:

- "It's normal to feel angry. We all feel like that sometimes."

- "I feel angry too when…"

- "I can tell when you are feeling angry (or frustrated or impatient). How can I help?"

- "I didn't know you felt so angry when…[something that makes your child angry]. How can I help?"

Anger Volcano and Erupting Lava Templates

Help your child create their own Anger Volcano

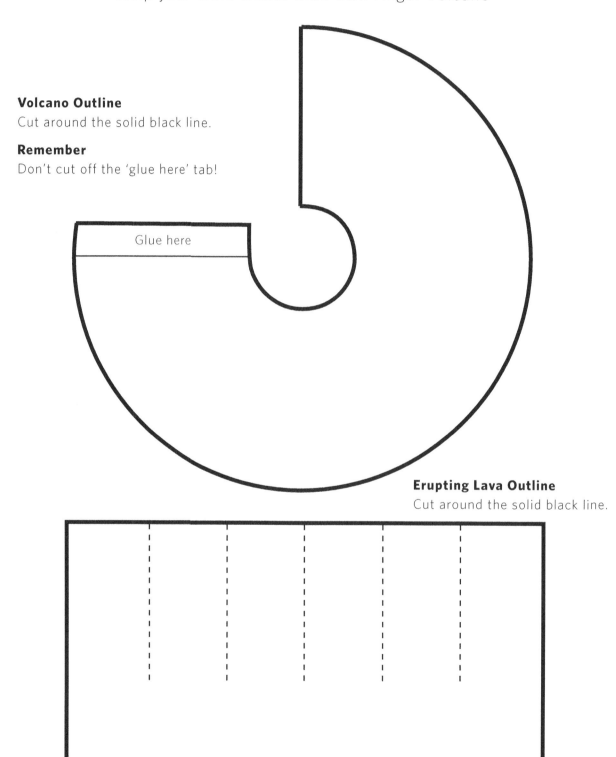

Volcano Outline
Cut around the solid black line.

Remember
Don't cut off the 'glue here' tab!

Glue here

Erupting Lava Outline
Cut around the solid black line.

Glitter Calm-Down Jars[*]

Ages 4–16

Create your own glitter calm-down jar for a soothing and relaxing resource to have at hand. Calm-down jars are fun to make and effective in helping children soothe themselves, breathe more deeply, and slow down.

Materials:

- A jar or plastic bottle (plastic is advisable for younger children)
- Warm water
- ½ cup glitter glue
- 3 drops of food coloring
- Glitter
- Whisk

Instructions:

1. Add warm water to your jar or bottle until it fills one third of the container.

2. Add the glitter glue into the container and stir until it is combined.

3. Add at least three drops of food coloring and stir. You can add more food coloring later if you'd like.

4. Pour in the glitter! You can use as much glitter as you would like. You can also add different types of glitter to give your jar more texture.

5. Finish your glitter calm-down jar by filling up the rest of the container with warm water until it is almost full. Be sure to leave a little gap at the top of the jar or bottle to allow the water to move.

---

[*] Adapted from https://www.goodtoknow.co.uk/family/things-to-do/glitter-jars-how-to-calm-down-jar-105300

When you talk about the glitter calm-down jar, you can say:

- "Everyone has really big, swirly, mixed-up feelings sometimes."

- "Sometimes we can be mad, frustrated, confused, and scared—all at the same time."

- "When you shake this glitter jar, the glitter swirls all around—just like your mind does when it fills up with all those big, swirly feelings. But let's see what happens when you stop shaking it."

- "Look: As you breathe and are still, both your mind and the glitter start to settle slowly and become calm again."

- "Breathe with whatever is going on, be still, and watch your big emotions as they gently float down."

Make Squiggle Drawings
Ages 6+

The squiggle drawing game is unlike more competitive and anxiety-provoking activities. There are no winners, losers, or finish lines to strive for. Indeed, you can just end when you feel like it. The easy, unstructured format is fun and relaxing. As you take turns watching each other dash off a squiggle, drawing imaginative pictures, hearing each other's stories, and enjoying yourselves, you will feel closer and more in the zone together. All you need for this activity is a lot of plain paper and some colored pencils or markers.

Instructions:

1. Make a scribble—called a "squiggle"—on a piece of paper. Keep it simple!

2. Hand it to your child and say, "Can you turn this squiggle into a picture of something?"

3. When your child is done with the drawing, ask her what it is. You can ask older kids to tell you a story about it, but don't be concerned if they don't want to do that.

4. Then ask your child to make a squiggle for you.

5. Turn that squiggle into a picture, and tell your child a little story about it. Perhaps build on a plot line she started when she described her picture. For example, if she made a dragon out of your squiggle, you might figure out how to make her squiggle into a cave where the dragon lives with his babies.

6. Notice her effort in creating a squiggle for you. (Is she trying to make it easy or challenging? Is she thinking hard or barely looking at the page?) Admire her focus and creativity as she turns your squiggle into a picture.

7. Do this a few times but stop before your child gets bored and tired so it will be a welcome idea to play again another day.

Make Funny Creatures
Ages 6+

This collaborative drawing activity also only requires some paper and pencils or markers to play. Making funny creatures is fun, easy, and more than a little bit silly. It's also wonderfully co-regulating. In the process of taking turns, making wild co-creations, and laughing together, you are all but guaranteed to feel cool, calm, and connected. And there is research to back up these claims: Children who engage in imaginative, interactive play with parents are, in fact, more likely to be emotionally regulated.

Instructions:

1. Get pencil or marker and a piece of paper on which each of you can draw.

2. Without showing your work, draw a head and neck at the top of the page. This can be a head and neck of a human, animal, or imaginative creature.

3. Fold the top of the paper down to hide your head and (most of the) neck, but let the bottom edges of the neck show.

4. Swap papers with your child.

5. Using the neck lines that are visible, but without looking at the concealed head, continue drawing the torso and arms of this evolving creature. Go as far as the waist of the creature.

6. Fold the top of the paper down to hide your torso and arms, but let the bottom edges of the torso show.

7. Swap again.

8. Using the torso lines that are visible, draw the waist to the knees. Fold the paper down, leaving the bottom edges of the knees visible.

9. Swap again.

10. Using the knee lines that are visible, complete the creature down to the feet. Fold the paper down and swap again.

11. Don't look yet. Name the creature in your hands.

12. Unfold the pieces of paper to reveal your combination creatures.

13. Spend time noticing the details and enjoying what you drew together.

Make Your Own Board Game
Ages 8–14

Designing a board game is a lot of fun; it's also a more sustained collaborative project that you can imagine and create together over a few weeks. An ongoing shared project like this is ideal for fostering co-regulation because it gives you and your child the opportunity to spend stretches of time anchored in safety together. The basic idea of the board game is this: Players role a die, land on a color, choose a matching color card, and then do what the card tells them to do. This game can be as simple or challenging as you desire. You can include obstacles and setbacks or make it a straight race from start to finish. That's all up to the design you come up with.

Materials:

- Roll of paper or huge poster board

- Construction paper

- Scissors

- Tape

- Glue

- Markers or pens

- Dice

- Game pieces (e.g., small objects or pieces taken from other board games, coins, etc.)

Instructions:

1. Roll out the paper to cover a table, or tape down the poster board.

2. Cut construction paper into squares (3×3 or 4×4 in size), making enough for two sets: one to cover the board to make a multicolored path and one for the game cards.

3. Together, create a path with the squares, deciding on the shape the path will take to get from start to finish.

4. Glue the squares to the paper or poster board to create the game board.

5. Brainstorm what the point of the game should be. What's the challenge that players face as they progress? Is it math facts, athletic feats, animal sounds and movements, challenging questions, anger management skills, sports trivia, family history, or some other area of interest and curiosity?

6. Write down all of the ideas, and try to come to an agreement about the point of the game. Give the game a name.

7. Leave most of the squares on the game board blank. Write on a few spaces that redirect the player to go forward or backward a space or two. Add a chance to roll again or to lose a turn if you so desire.

8. Come up with tasks to do on the colored playing cards. For example, if your board game is about animals, you might designate the pink cards for acting like a particular animal or the blue cards for answering questions about animal behavior.

9. Decide on the rules of the game: Who goes first? What happens if someone doesn't know how to answer a question or doesn't want to? Can you pass, take a different card of that same color, or ask for help?

10. Play by rolling the die and moving your game piece the corresponding number of spaces.

11. When you land on a colored square, choose a playing card of the same color. Perform the task on that card.

12. In points of contention, stop playing and refine the rules.

13. Only play the game if it's fun. The design and creation of the game is as important as the actual experience of playing it.

Make Your Own Jigsaw Puzzle
Ages 9–13

Some people love to puzzle together. It's a side-by-side activity that requires shared attention and interest. It can be comforting to sit near someone you love without having to look at them or answer lots of direct questions. The companionable silence and puzzle-based chit-chat will feel regulating for both of you. In this version of puzzling, you will both be creating and solving the puzzle. Perhaps you could decide on a scene that illustrates "our family doing something together." It may be meaningful, but not essential, to depict something personal in your collaborative puzzle.

Materials:

- An old floor puzzle or well-made table puzzle you and your child can solve and are ready to part with (If the pieces hold together well, you can just flip it over and paint your puzzle on the back. If you want to use the front where there is already a picture, plan on covering it over with a white base coat first.)

- White paint

- Acrylic paint

- Pencil and paper

- Optional: Masking tape (helps with straight lines and keeps puzzle from moving)

Instructions:

1. Find a floor or table puzzle you can repurpose for this project.

2. Assemble the puzzle and paint over the front with white base paint, or flip it over so you can paint the back.

3. Use paper to discuss and sketch out your plans for the puzzle scene. Agree on the tasks each of you will take on for designing and painting the scene.

4. Use a pencil to transfer the sketch to the side of the puzzle that is painted white.

5. Paint the puzzle.

6. When it dries, take it apart and assemble it together.

Inside/Outside Boxes
Ages 9+

In this powerful activity, you and your child will have an opportunity to explore the important question: Who am I? When we can take a good look at ourselves—and feel seen by someone we love—we develop a new perspective on who we are. Given that increased self-awareness is a cornerstone of regulation, big feelings are also less likely to take over when we have a clearer sense of self. Dysregulated kids often feel ashamed, inadequate, and unable to be fully themselves in front of other people. Using inside/outside boxes, you and your child will both have the opportunity to explore how you each view yourself, as well as how you believe others view you.

Materials:

- 2 shoeboxes (one for each of you)

- Glue

- Scissors

- Old magazines to use for collage material

Instructions:

1. Decorate the outside of the box:

   - Spend time looking through the magazines, and find different words and pictures that represent how you believe *others* view you. Cut them out. Feel free to offer suggestions to each other—and to turn down words and images that you don't think fit with how people see you.

   - Glue these words and images on the outside of your box, as well as to the box's lid, to make a collage.

2. Decorate the inside of the box:

   - Repeat this process, but find words and pictures that represent how *you* see yourself, including your strengths, weaknesses, identity, fears, and dreams.

3. After you are done collaging, spend time thinking about what it's like seeing the outside of your box in comparison to the inside of your box.

4. Talk about each of your boxes. How well do you know each other? What feelings come up when you look at the difference between how you feel inside and the way you think people see you? Are there surprises? What is it like to have your inside and outside selves be different?

Life Map
Ages 4+

A life map is a visual timeline of someone's life. In this activity, you will be helping your child create his own life map, starting when he was born and continuing with significant moments in his life up until the present day. Allow your child to choose the events and experiences he would like to record on his life map—for example, birth and adoption dates, significant holidays and vacations, the start of school, the adoption of a pet, the birth of a sibling, a move, parents' divorce, a significant injury, or the death of someone close to him.

You can help him with memories and stories, and if you have photos of life events that he'd like to include on the life map, a few of those would be great to have nearby. If he doesn't remember events and expresses curiosity about them, fill him in on details. For example, he may not recall something interesting that happened on his sixth birthday or the house he lived in when he was a baby. The goal is to have him assemble the events that have been most important to him and to have conversations that fill in some of the details about those key experiences.

There is a profound connection between a coherent identity narrative and emotional regulation. Children who are more regulated share three things in common: (1) They hold a self-story that makes logical, chronological sense. They remember a range of events that bring up all kinds of feelings. (2) The events in the story and the feelings go together. They are able to remember the happy events happily and feel sad about the hard times. (3) They do not hold this story alone; they have someone who remembers it too—or who wants to hear all about it. As a corollary, kids who have endured adverse childhood experiences are more likely to have identity narratives that seem disorganized and feel confusing to them. Creating a life map together is one way to fill in gaps in the identity story and to support greater emotional regulation.

Materials:

- A piece of paper large enough for a life map (It should be long enough so there is plenty of room for future experiences that haven't been filled in yet. You can also make a life book and extend the line over the bottom of several pages, leaving lots of blank sheets in the back.)

- Pens, pencils, and markers

- Decorative items, such as photographs, stickers, cards, and clippings

Instructions:

1. Make a long horizontal line running the length of the paper.

2. Start the life map on the day your child was born.

3. Label each event in the order it occurred. If your child remembers events out of order, help organize the memories in the correct sequence by discussing them with him.

4. If you know dates of these events, you can include them on the map.

5. Illustrate the events with photos and drawings.

6. Add captions to the photos, such as "On the first day of school, I had a huge new bookbag."

7. Leave room for speculation about the future: "What do you think will happen next year, in five years, or when you are 21 or 50?"

Some helpful conversation starters to have when discussing the life map:

- "How did you choose these events?"

- "I also remember when... On that day, I remember..."

- "I am amazed that you remember grandpa's funeral so well. You were only 5 years old!"

- "What else do you remember about meeting your baby brother for the first time?"

Alter Ego Masks
Ages 8–14

An alter ego is an alternative version of yourself that has some powers you wish you possessed. It has a lot more fun in life than you do. For example, if you or your child second-guess yourself a lot—or if you feel stupid, don't like to take risks, fret about what people will think, worry about being laughed at, or don't feel brave enough, smart enough, or strong enough to do things—then creating your alter ego will give you the opportunity to break out of your normal ways of thinking about yourself.

If either of you are you having trouble thinking of the right alter ego for you, here are some questions to consider:

- What kind of personality would you like to have?

- What kind of mindset would you like to be in?

- What would you want your alter ego to look like?

- What would your alter ego's superpowers be?

- What name would you like to be called?

After you think about these questions, start designing your mask, and give your secret superpowers a chance to have some fun. Design your mask to show all of the qualities your alter ego possesses. If either of you are still wondering about this activity, give it a try anyway. Creativity usually leads us in the right direction. You might even discover you have a much more interesting relationship when you find that you are not just interacting with each other, but with your alter egos, too!

Materials:

- Cardboard
- Acrylic paint
- Paint brushes
- Scissors or box cutter
- Markers
- Glue
- String or stretchy elastic (to secure the mask over your face)
- Optional crafts: pom-poms, feathers, ribbon, or stickers

Instructions:

1. Cut a face shape out of the piece of cardboard.

2. Draw two eyes with a marker on the back of the cardboard. Pay attention to the placement so your eyes line up with mask holes.

3. Cut the eyes out with scissors or a box cutter.

4. Decorate your mask using paint, markers, stickers, pom-poms, and other craft options.

5. If you are interested, you can glue cardboard strips around the mask or glue yarn to look like hair. Whatever makes you feel most like your alter ego.

6. To finish off your mask, knot string or stretchy elastic through the eye holes to loop around the back of your head.

7. If you'd like, give your alter ego a name.

Some helpful questions to ask when discussing the alter ego mask:

- "What is your alter ego like?"

- "When would you like to be your alter ego, and when would you like to be yourself?"

- "Are there any times you and your alter ego have felt like one and the same?"

- "What do you think would be fun or challenging if we both turned into our alter egos at the same time?"

Wishing Tree[*]
All ages

In this craft activity, you will be making a wishing tree, which will expand with your wishes for yourself, your family, your friends, and the world. This wishing tree is intended to help both you and your child grow in kindness over time. Too many days of struggle on end can make it harder for you to feel loving and generous toward each other. The wishing tree creates an intentional shift in focus toward regulating care and connection.

Set a time each day, perhaps before bedtime, to think about this question: If you could make one wish for anyone in the world, what would it be? Write it down and add your wish to the tree. Watch your tree bloom!

Materials:

- Paper grocery bag
- Scissors
- Masking tape
- Sticky notes
- Pens
- Pencil

Instructions:

1. Cut through the sides of the paper bag to create a long rectangle.

2. Draw an outline of a tree with branches on the inside of the bag.

3. Cut out your tree shape.

4. Crinkle the tree up into a ball, and then smooth it back out to add bark-like texture.

5. Tape your tree to a door or wall.

6. Write out a wish on a sticky note—you can cut your note into the shape of a flower if you would like—and post it to a branch.

---

* Adapted from https://www.doinggoodtogether.org/bhf/create-a-wishing-tree

7. Set aside a time each day to add new wishes to your wishing tree.

8. Try to make this a daily practice, and encourage your child to think about wishes for himself, others in the family, his friends, the community, the country, and the world.

Some helpful conversation starters to have when you are creating a wishing tree:

- "What made you choose this particular wish today?"

- "Your wish made me think about..."

- "I felt _____ when I saw your wish today."

- "I had the same wish as you. What do you think of that?"

Conclusion

One of my daughters called me on the phone yesterday, just to gab. She told me about her adorable dog and asked me about my work. We discussed politics, the latest family doings, and the change of the seasons. It was not the most profound or memorable exchange, but when the call ended, I recognized a feeling of great warmth and calm deep in my belly. Nowadays, more often than not, conversations with my kids are thoroughly nourishing, just like this. No matter how I am feeling earlier, I end up feeling safely anchored—deep in the zone—when I just hear their familiar, heartwarming voices.

I tell you this not to brag (well, maybe a little) but to promise you that your children will grow up eventually too and that the old cliché is true: One day, sooner than you think, you'll maybe even miss some of this insanity.

Even when you feel completely stuck in the quicksand of family life, your kids are still secretly developing and changing a tiny bit every day. I'm sure that if I were struggling about brushing teeth or smartphones for the zillionth time as you are, I wouldn't be able to see how it all works out either—but I write as a survivor, so perhaps you can believe me when I tell you it won't stay this way forever. And while I do remember how utterly exhausting it can be to parent day in and out, the details have mostly disappeared or become almost comical in the rearview mirror. Was she actually upset that there was a sprig of parsley on her noodles? Was I really that irritated when one sister tried to glue the other's door shut? (Yes and yes.)

I didn't study much about co-regulation 30 years ago, but as you have probably figured out, I'm deep in it now—and if you have read this far, so are you. It isn't that complicated when you think about it. To sum up the whole workbook, all the activities and explanations really boil down to these five big ideas:

1. **You are your child's co-regulator**. Sometimes it's almost impossible not to get caught up in your child's emotionality, but that's your important work. When you start to take this part of your job seriously, your intentionality will become a resource for you in all aspects of your life. Every time you can be less reactive in a struggle, the interaction will go better.

2. **It's not your child's job to help you feel better**. Our lives would be easier if our kids self-soothed and behaved well, but that probably won't happen today. Indeed, today you are the adult in possession of a fully developed brain, and your child is an immature human being who needs you to be okay when she is not.

3. **Co-regulation precedes self-regulation.** We all want our kids to learn to calm down on their own and to think clearly when they're upset. To develop these self-soothing and problem-solving skills, they first need to know what regulation feels like. They need a cool, calm, and connected you. This capacity for self-comforting takes time, even under the most optimal life circumstances; children who have endured trauma and loss will take longer to develop it.

4. **You can't co-regulate until you feel regulated yourself.** Emotion is contagious, and regulation is too. But it requires a lot of conscious intention to stay in the zone while your kid falls to pieces. It makes sense that emotionality and distress often win in families, but it is undeniably better for everyone when calmer heads prevail.

5. **Even the best self-soothers need help sometimes.** No matter our age or skill level, we all face challenges in our lives that overwhelm our capacity to manage on our own. This includes you and me, as well as our kids—and everyone else. We are evolutionarily wired to need one another for care. To be an effective co-regulator for your child, you will also need people on whom *you* can depend.

Your challenge now is to try to grow up alongside your challenging kids—to change and develop too. I've given you many ideas about how to think differently about yourself and your relationship, and perhaps you are already acting more intentionally and compassionately. I hope so. If you are, I hope, too, that you are beginning to see the fruits of your efforts and have more stretches when you feel regulated yourself. It's a practice to stay cool, calm, and connected, and our kids generously give us plenty of opportunities to get better at it.

Made in the USA
Las Vegas, NV
13 July 2023

74598283R00096